WATER AND THE CYCLE OF LIFE

BY THE SAME AUTHOR:

Weeds: Guardians of the Soil
Farming with Nature
Trampling Out the Vintage

WATER

and the Cycle of Life

JOSEPH A. COCANNOUER

THE DEVIN-ADAIR COMPANY

NEW YORK 🐎 1962

This book
is cordially dedicated
to a true friend
of water conservation:
GOVERNOR RAYMOND GARY
of Oklahoma

Foreword

Over the years, Joseph A. Cocannouer has given much to many people. It has been particularly gratifying to have known him and to have traveled over vast areas of the land with him, discussing nature and her own ways of solving our soil and water problems. Almost daily he has made it a habit to stop by my clinic where he sees me trying to combat tooth decay for an endless array of patients, especially children. A few years ago I suggested to him that the right kind of water might be as necessary for my patients as the right kind of food. With this he enthusiastically agreed, and this new book is the result of that discussion.

His book has something of interest for every living person. Each chapter deals with problems that are paramount today in the minds of all thinking Americans—especially those with a stake in the land—the gardener, the farmer, the future farmers and the many wild-life enthusiasts. Each of these will find much of great value. Then there is also an important health angle. Quality food and quality water constitute most important topics today. The author stresses the need for civic organizations in cities both large and small to begin making a survey of their food and water problems—*now, before it is too late.* This feature will be of particular interest to all municipal leaders.

May God bless Joseph A. Cocannouer, who over the years has enriched our lives and is continuing to do so by giving to us all, and to posterity in particular, the benefit of what he has learned in a lifetime of observing nature at first hand.

LLOYD E. CHURCH, D.D.S.

Wilburton, Oklahoma

Preface

Material for this book has come from many sources and from more than sixty years of water study as a naturalist. My knowledge of water in its relation to the soil, to the plant, and to the animal—which includes man himself—has been gleaned from the jungle man and his water knowledge and beliefs, as well as from my Pennsylvania Dutch ancestors who, probably more than any other pioneer American settlers, thoroughly understood the meaning of Quality Water.

I wish to pay particular homage to a great water book and to its many authors: the 1955 Year Book of the United States Department of Agriculture. During its many years of existence the Department has brought out a great number of volumes of scientific agricultural information; but, to me, that outstanding reference work on water surpasses them all. It should have a conspicuous place in every library—and should not be permitted to gather dust.

One of our greatest needs in America today is not merely *more* water; our chief need is *quality* water for human consumption. Therefore, the theme of this book is quality water and the means of obtaining it. Only when we abide by the laws of nature's own water pattern is quality water possible. The aim of this book is to chart nature's straight and narrow road to her zones of conditioned, quality water.

The glossary at the back of the book will be of help to those who are in doubt about the definitions of certain terms used.

J. A. C.

Contents

WATER AND THE CYCLE OF LIFE

1 Water Concepts

The mailman brought me a letter and I hurriedly tore it open. "Joe, I want you to come up," my friend wrote. "I've got so many things to show you, so many things to talk about! And they're coming back, Joe the springs! Not too much yet, but they're coming—just what I've been waiting for all these years. Springs of cool, clear water—we're going to have them!"

More letters came, all expressing the same enthusiasm— the enthusiasm of the supreme naturalist who could read the signs. Yes, springs of quality water gurgling through draws and gullies that had been dry so long. Springs that were abiding by nature's water pattern!

Water naturalist that I was, it was too much for me to resist, so I prepared for a visit with one of our great present-day soil students; a naturalist who knew his "dirt" as few others. Then, only two days before I was to leave, came the news. Death had claimed one of my truest friends.

Louie Bromfield was gone. He was to have written the foreword to this book. Another, a loyal friend of us both, has taken his place, and ably. But Bromfield's spirit is in the book; as it will long be throughout our land.

Bromfield's water concept was right.

What is your concept of water? Do you think of water as a loyal friend, or as a savage foe? Or perhaps both?

Have you ever seen a sudden flood come sweeping through a valley and carry a house and all its sleeping inmates to a watery death? If you have, you'll probably unconsciously hate water forever after: cruelly destructive water, in many lands a perpetual curse ever since the beginning of human history; water on the loose, uncontrolled and uncontrollable. Yet, as we shall see, man has brought that curse upon himself.

Consider the white man lost in the jungle, a man inexperienced in nature's wisdom. Water is all about him, but he is dying of thirst. It was the parched time of the year and he had not been able to find a trickle, not even a foul pool. When he was close to death a jungle native discovered him. The native found a bamboo cane nearby and drawing his large knife cut it down. He removed a certain joint from the cane, slashed it open, and tipped the joint to the dying man's lips. Water! Abundance of quality water from a bamboo cane.

What was this white man's water concept to be thenceforth? After he had come back to civilization, his craving for "bamboo water" was so insistent that he finally cut loose his ties and returned to the jungle. When I next saw him he had gone native—and was thoroughly contented. After drinking bamboo water with him I could almost understand why, although I had not gone through the same ordeal.

I knew another man who had almost died of thirst. Help came to him in the barren wasteland when his tongue was swollen, his eyes glazed. They gave him a drop of water at a time, living drop after living drop, and out of indescribable torture a wild joy came springing. To that man, water ever after was to be the most beautiful thing his mind could conceive. "Since that experience," he said to me, "I never have felt safe except in the immediate presence of water. It's impossible to describe the feeling. If I'm near water, even a little mudhole, I have absolutely no fear of anything: storm, fire, ferocious animal, man. Floods give me a feeling of odd delight. You can't understand this; nobody can understand it. When it is time for me to go, I pray that I may die in water!"

There have been times when I could almost understand that water concept.

To the jungle savage, water is a friendly god; fire is a god of fear. During the dry period, I have seen flames race across tropical grasslands and turn the jungle itself into an inferno. I have seen a searing red bank of fire swallow whole villages within a few minutes. I have seen screaming people flee for safety, and once or twice have heard the last cries of unfortunate ones left behind.

A crocodile-infested river would then become a haven of refuge. Mothers with infants in their arms would plunge into the perilous waters and feel relatively safe.

When typhoons rage and water pours from the skies, jungle people dance in the rain and shout for joy because their water god has returned. The jungle floor may be an endless lake, yet the forest will be wild with rasping song: the rains have come to put an end to the cruelties of the fire god. Now the fish will move up into the rivers from the sea, and there will be abundance of rice and vegetables in the little fields.

In the far north, there are endless stretches of frozen water in all directions. To the person unfamiliar with those regions, the picture is one of ever-threatening death. But, to the Eskimo, it is a living white world of promise. Only his trained eye can detect the polar bear on the distant ice cliff; only he can see the snow rabbit. In his snow hut, wife and children expectantly await his return from the hunt and make preparations for the feast. To the Eskimo, as to the jungle man, water is life.

In our temperate zone too, water is life; life for plant, lower animal, man. And it is food for all. But it is not food in the true sense unless it adheres to nature's complete pattern. As we shall see in later chapters, it is complete quality water only if it is sent down into the earth, there to be conditioned according to basic, invariable laws. If it follows the road that nature has marked out, it becomes nutritious water. It is undefiled, it obeys nature's water laws, and it does not mount into flood and raging disaster.

2 "Whatsoever a man soweth . . ."

In subsequent chapters we shall consider the water ideals of nature under primitive conditions. When man enters the scene, changes come fast and not always for the best. For there is a law as invariable as the stars: "Whatsoever a man soweth that shall he also reap." One day . . .

The sun rose dry and ominous. A threatening hush hung over everything. People went about their morning tasks with that weird feeling which once in a while seemed to come over one in the dust bowl.

"Well, guess maybe this is going to be it!" someone said.

Understand? No; you never will unless you have gone through one of those choking dust storms.

By ten o'clock tiny whirlwinds of dust were numerous on the unprotected fields. On the plowed and unplanted land they resembled an army of whirling dervishes. By one o'clock in the afternoon the dust was rising from the loose soil like a billowing blanket and the sun was covered over. By four, visibility was zero. "Hell in the air!" some called it. Strangling, torturing, waterless acres lifting themselves and just floating away.

Night came early. The wind drove the dust like needles against everything in its path. Drivers unable to reach home sought shelter where they could. Many were forced to stop their cars at the roadside. They couldn't shut out the dust, however. It seeped in like a fog through the smallest cracks; poured into ears and eyes and nostrils. Throats grew parched. And there was no water! No water to keep the nostrils and throat from clogging with mud. Not a drop of water! (It had never been like this before the short-grass sod was broken). God, give us water! How can one breathe with nostrils and throat closed!

Jim Estes was trying to make it to his line fence. He tied a handkerchief over his nose and mouth and crawled out of the car. The wind caught the car door and slammed it back. He finally reached the fence, after a struggle. The dust-laden wind drove against him with such force he had little control of his movements, even by clinging to the fence. He couldn't see an inch in front of him. He'd have to make it to water pretty quick, or else. A gust of wind jerked his hands from the wire. He dropped on all fours and crawled to the next post, grasping the wires more firmly. He could feel the blood in his palms from the barb punctures.

Blindly he went on. His throat was aflame now. At first the posts hadn't seemed so far apart. Now they were miles from each other. If he only had one swallow of water! The handkerchief he had tied over his face was weighted down with mud. He had never imagined there were so many posts in that fence! If he could only see a little! He didn't dread the draw so much; that draw he was going to have to cross —if he ever got there. There was no fence across the draw; crossing over to find the first post on the other side was going to cause the trouble. Once he had located that first post he could follow the fence to the corner of the barn.

Jim didn't know he had reached the draw until he stumbled over the edge. He had crossed that draw so often he could do it on the darkest night without a flash. But he had never until now been forced to cross it in a dust storm! He turned his back to the wind and tried to cough some of the mud out of his throat. Then he stumbled down the bank to the dry stream bed. The wind was a little less savage now.

He knew that the first post of the east fence was up there someplace. He felt his way across to the bank and started up. The wind bombarded him again. But the meager shrubbery was of some help; it gave him something to cling to. As he moved slowly up the bank, Jim was forced to use all his thinking power to keep his feet on the ground. Suddenly he realized he couldn't tell whether he had been leaning more to the right or to the left. At last he felt the rim and scrambled up onto the level. But to which side of the post was he?

He decided to crawl along the rim to the right. On his hands and knees the wind wasn't quite so vicious. But after he had crawled what seemed like miles, it was clear to him that he had made the wrong choice. Wearily he turned back. And crawled and crawled. In the name of heaven—if he just had one swallow of water! And still no post! Choking, he lay down with his face on his arm. His nostrils were completely clogged; and his throat—Jim Estes knew there would be no breathing through that either, not for many more minutes. So this was what it meant to die in a dust storm; without water!

Never before had Jim ever been forced to realize the true value of water. What just a few drops could mean to him now! Guess this was it. Funny thing about that, too. Every dust storm he had been through he had wondered how it would feel to be caught out and forced to die in a dust blizzard. Yes, forced to die—and for the want of only a few drops of water!

Then Jim caught the bark of his dog. He heard it though his ears were full of dust. Next thing old Dan was licking his face and whining as if to tell him not to give up. It took his faithful old dog to bring back his courage. Jim staggered to his feet, touched Dan, and sank his fingers into his long hair. Dan then turned and started for the barn—along the fence that was only a yard or so from where Jim had given up.

Jim Estes had a different concept of water from then on.

On another day . . .

There had been the rumble of distant thunder since shortly before noon; then the black cloud showed itself peering over the horizon of the northwest. But the cloud was moving slowly, and dusk might fall before there was any serious disturbance. Around three the cloud began to

increase its speed. It swept to the zenith, then dropped to
the eastern and southeastern horizons. By now, lightning
was constant and thunderbolts came fast and furious. One
funnel was sighted, but fortunately it didn't come down.
There were a few minutes of robin's-egg hail; then the
rain. Within seconds the water was pouring down in
sheets. It was flowing across the already-eroded slopes and
rushing down the gullies—water that was red and slimy
and thick. Like hell on the rampage it was. It gnawed at
the bowels of dying land. It rumbled into a ravine, and the
ravine soon became a soupy river that boiled on into the
rapidly filling larger stream.

It wasn't long before the roar of this creek told that it
was out of its banks. The thick water crawled across once-
rich bottoms and spread over them a coating of dead
earth. (There had been a time when floods didn't sweep
across those bottoms save after an occasional cloudburst, a
time down there when the soil was deep and mellow;
quality soil that produced quality crops. Nobody farmed
the dead bottoms now. The farmer who owned those bottoms moved to town because his two wells had dropped so
low there was no longer enough water for house use. He's
running a delivery wagon for a small grocery.)

Word had gotten round in town; everybody was jubi-
lant: the long-delayed rains had come at last and were
filling the city lake. The lake was filling fast; it was already
up to the spillway. The news was the most satisfying ever
—to the folks in town. People rushed out to the lake, right
in the pouring rain. Imagine—water at last! After all the
skimping and rationing—abundance of water! It was a
beautiful sight: rippling red slush; streams of yellow vomit

gushing into the lake on three sides, and as it entered the lake it built hillocks of pink-red foam.

People sang and danced in the rain; embraced each other; scooped the red soup into their hands. Water—water at last! Bring on the chemicals and we'll have quality water! Hurry to the hospital and tell them to make ready—water is coming! Nutritious water for the sick! Health-carrying water! But don't fail to tell the undertakers they'd better increase their supply of coffins!

(Nature weeps at man's ignorance; yet men continue to ignore her. Instead of listening to reason, man continues to drink drugged water—drugged erosion slush—and continues to build more hospitals; and as an aftermath he continues to add acres to his graveyards. Ignorance! Selfishness! Eroded land! Wrecked water cycle—and nations sink into oblivion.)

The silt-laden creeks had been pouring into the rivers; the small rivers dumping their burdens into the larger ones. The Missouri and Ohio were groaning under their unwelcome loads. (The oldest Indians had known well the great river of the sunrise and the great river of the sunset. But they had never known destructive floods until the arrival of the paleface.)

Rich and poor labored in the mud and rain. In the name of reason, would the crest ever go by? Many had been on the job for twenty-seven hours without respite, save to grab a few morsels of food. But for every inch they raised the dyke, the river countered with another inch in height. Hurry, men! More dirt! If it once breaks through we're gone! Don't stop to eat—don't stop for anything! Bring us dirt—more bags of sand! Anything you can get your hands on!

Equals they were now; dwellers in mansion and hovel fighting for something more than their own lives. And the river continued to rise!

A preacher knelt in the mud, one hand dangling in the dark river flow. He prayed: "Don't forget us now, God! In the name of Christ—come to our rescue! We've done our best, God! Father in heaven—if that dyke breaks, you know what will happen to us all. . . ."

Rain poured the harder. Lightning flashes outglared the flicker of the flashlights.

Hurry, men! It's slopping over here! In the name of God, hurry! It's beginning to break. . . .

The preacher's prayer was a shout of despair now: "Father, take me if you will, but save those people down there in the bottoms! Oh Father in heaven, have mercy on us now. . . ."

More bags, men! It's spilling over again! It's cutting through! Sandbags! Sandbags! If it gains an inch on us here we'll never stop it! In the name of God, hurry. . . !

The preacher stood up; reached his arms toward the dark waters. "Father, we can do no more! You alone can save us in this last moment of desperation. . . ."

A man was shouting from high up on the bank—"The dam up river has given way! A solid mountain of water is coming! Run for your lives. . . !"

Two or three of those at the dyke were too late. Several of those still clinging to their lowly homes in the flats below were also too late. The bellowing of the cattle in the marooned stock cars was sickening—until the flood had silenced the cries.

The muddy flood fingers were relentless. The thick water crawled up out of the flats, up well-kept streets, into the first floors of aristocratic homes. People fled with the few precious belongings they were able to carry.

Daylight presented a horrible sight: the wake of the receding flood. Many learned for the first time that reaping does follow the sowing. And they had a new concept of water!

Several old Indians sat silently around the one remaining spring. The Indians were sad; for redmen, they were terribly sad. The water dripped from the great sand boulder, but not as it had dripped in the old days, when the tribe camped near this spring because of its abundance. One of the old redmen was dreaming. He was dreaming of those long-ago years. He was very wrinkled now; his own years were more than he could count. His memory was very keen, though, and he liked to talk to those who could understand; to talk about the Father of Waters and its tributaries, the Missouri and the Ohio. He had not sent his own canoe up the Ohio, but his grandfather had. Old High Eagle, after whom he was named.

Young High Eagle would tell us, his beady eyes revealing a strange bitterness, how he and his companion warriors, in their youth, drove their canoes up the river of the sunset, even after the white man had arrived. It often had rained hard then, and there were floods, but the great river rarely broke from its banks. The water was almost clear then, and the fish so plentiful one could harvest them with a basket. That was the Missouri before the white man had taken over completely.

Young High Eagle had witnessed one of the modern Missouri floods; a flood that had poured destruction into four large towns and several smaller ones. It pained him to tell about it: the river he had loved so devoutly in his youth now a killer beast. The Arkansas also he had known well in his younger years—when there was little mud in its waters and no white-man pollution either. But it was the Little River that had been nearest the heart of young High Eagle: the Cimarron. His ancient eyes would grow moist and his words would almost fail him when he would talk about the Cimarron; and what oil had done to it. It was only then that young High Eagle revealed his hatred for the white man. The paleface had been a fool. The squaws could have told the white man how to treat his rich land. Now the soil from the uplands had come down to poison the Little River, and the Arkansas, and the great river of the sunset. Of course, oil had been the greatest calamity in the Little River and the Arkansas country. The Little River was dead and, in the eyes of High Eagle, it was oil and eroded soil that had killed it.

Young High Eagle now sleeps in a grave known to few. The Ohio, the Arkansas, the Missouri, the Cimarron, and many other large streams that were once part of the Indian's own private world are now carriers of erosion slush, of pollution. It is well that the redmen of that grand past now sleep, ignorant of the wreckage brought about in so many instances by white-man negligence.

Yes, whatever a man soweth, he must reap accordingly! Human ignorance and selfishness have forced constructive nature to become a destructive fiend. The soil segment of her water cycle is a wreck, clear across our land. Erosion slush instead of nutritious, quality water is now the usual harvest. When we add to this the curse of direct man pollution, the words of High Eagle ring true: "The white man is a fool!"

Civilization and pollution come close to being synonymous terms. The contamination of our rivers is making one of the blackest pages of American history. Pouring city filth into our streams has long been a regular custom. The savage, in any land, is far more considerate of his own well-being. He protects his drinking water as a common practice.

Even the most intelligent people rarely stop to realize what the pollution of our larger streams has done to our wildlife. The destruction of beneficial wildlife in this manner has been staggering. Soil erosion has done its part, but city filth and commercial waste have been even more malignant. I like to think of the Cimarron River in Oklahoma as a challenging example of what contamination can do to a primeval river teeming with fish. High Eagle, my Indian friend, did not live to see the worst. In my youth the Cimarron was a fisherman's paradise. Then came oil and the human craze for gold at no matter what cost. Soon the black filth was seeping into the river, and soon the fish were dying in huge numbers. Today the Cimarron, so far as its once-famous wildlife is concerned, does not exist. The few hardy fish that one may occasionally catch are so tainted with oil they are scarcely edible.

No matter where the pollution may come from—from oil or city waste or as the byproduct of a factory—the results are much the same: fish and other wildlife poisoned; human health dangerously threatened. Even in rural sections, pollution may become a subtle danger. An example will illustrate that this is more common than most people think. A successful farmer, an active worker against general pollution in his community, often boasted about his fine well of quality water. When I was near the well one day and observed its location, I immediately became suspicious. The well was situated below the barnlot, and a little exploring revealed a continuous flow of "filthy albumen" from animal manure, which seeped into the well during every hard rain. A naturally fine well had been turned into a pest hole through human ignorance.

Pollution apathy has long been a curse in our nation. People must come to know that safe water and sound health are inseparable. It may not always be easy to obtain nutritious quality water, but there is no excuse for deliberately contaminating the water we have. Every human being in our country should become conscious of the basic laws of nature and recognize as a practical matter his relationship to those laws.

In nature's growth cycle there is little or no waste. That is to say that city garbage should, wherever possible, be processed into "soil food" and then employed in helping to rebuild our eroded lands. To rebuild the land means repairing the soil segment of the water cycle. It means to eliminate the health menace and to go far toward preparing our soils for the production of health-carrying foods. Safe water means quality food. We can go a long way toward having both by whipping erosion and pollution.

Nature is always kind when we heed her. She is ever

ready to help us repair the wreckage which we have brought about. Therefore the road back is clear: soil-water conservation and control of contamination wherever it exists. Nature's soil pattern must be returned to our land, for only then will the water cycle function according to Nature's Togetherness Law.

3 Nature's Water Cycle

"Darkness was upon the face of the deep" (Gen. 1:2).

Before there could be ocean depths there had to be rain—and in the beginning there was no rain. Geologists tell us that the earth was at first a molten mass, probably enveloped in a cloud of hot vapor. In due course the earth's crust evolved, with a temperature below the boiling point. That cloud of vapor began to condense and give birth to the rains. It is likely that those first rains were prodigious; the water must have come down in sheets and continuously. There were floods beyond our present conception of the word.

In the meantime the earth in its cooling developed wrinkles, and these gave rise to mountains and valleys and plains. The floods poured into the valleys and inundated the low areas. Thus our oceans were born; vast expanses of clear, unsalted water. For millennia our oceans and seas probably contained fresh water. Though the rainfall was tremendous, there was little erosion because there was no soil to erode. But the rocks did gradually break down, and slowly but persistently they sent their minerals to the fresh-water seas and in due time changed them to brine.

These cataclysmic changes took place in almost complete darkness. No sunlight was able to penetrate to the earth until that envelope of vapor had dissipated itself. When the light did reach the earth, a new phase in the course of events moved in: water began to rise again from the oceans in the form of vapor, causing a new kind of rain cloud to appear in the earth's atmosphere.

More eons went by, while rock sediment spread a layer over our planet's surface—the beginning of the soil blanket that was to come a long time later.

Now mystery takes over: the beginning of organic life. It is generally accepted that the first protoplasm—the substance of that first organic life consisting largely of water and minerals—had its inception in the oceans: not during the first rainfalls that gushed into the broad valleys, but after minerals had been disintegrated in quantity from the rocks and carried to the seas.

First came plant life of a low order; then comparable animal life. Mark the wisdom of nature! There could be no animals until there were plants to provide them with nourishment. Today the more complex animal protoplasm is as dependent upon plants for its nourishment as it was on the day of its origin in those ancient seas.

Even after plants and animals, over the ages, moved from

the sea and adapted themselves to a land mode of existence, their composition did not change materially. They continued to consist, as does every living thing today, largely of water. Consequently, an all-wise nature would be expected to provide abundantly and efficiently for maintaining the water content of the protoplasm of her land life. This she has done through her Water Cycle.

Before we wade more deeply into nature's water cycle, two staggering, related questions confront us. Is there any loss in nature's water supply, in the broad scheme of things? And is there any phase of the water cycle in which nature creates water? Here we run up against two unsettled theories. One, that nature does create water to replace the water that is broken down to build food in the leaf's food factory. This theory maintains that nature must create water if she is to maintain her water balance —for maintaining balances is a basic law of nature. After all, it's easy enough to combine the two gases hydrogen and oxygen in the laboratory and produce the water molecule. Does nature do this, then, as one of her fundamental water laws?

There are those who insist that she does not. Their theory is that in the dim and distant future all water on the earth will have been used up. Organic life will vanish then, and earth will become cold and silent. However, there is nothing to gain by worrying about it. We're not forgetting, too, that nature's balances must enter in somewhere. After pondering the question for a long moment, a wise scientist once remarked dryly: "Quite likely the insects will have destroyed all other organic life long before that dismal day arrives."

Nature works in cycles. The growth cycle is from seed to seed; the water cycle from sea to sea. Cycle means circle, and, in following a circle, it doesn't make much difference where you start. So let us begin the water cycle with the broad expanse of the oceans, which had such a tumultuous beginning.

From the surface of the sea invisible masses of vapor are forever moving upward through the atmosphere. This vapor flow from the sea maintains a fairly constant saturation of the upper air—the birthplace of our modern rains which sometimes are not too unlike those "showers" of the long ago. And the cradles of our rains are the clouds, formed from the rising vapor. Most of us are familiar with several kinds of clouds, but the clouds we're chiefly interested in now are the water carriers, of which probably the most commonly known in the temperate zone are the cumulus.

Of course, most disturbances in the upper air are traceable to wind movements produced by the earth whirling upon its axis. However, when speaking of local conditions, it is not far wrong to say that when a cold air current strikes a mass of warm air, the vapor condenses until rain-carrying clouds are formed. Such clouds are sometimes composed of a mixture of water vapor and ice crystals; or raindrops may form around dust particles, until little water masses are developed which fall to earth.

Thunderstorms are old familiars to most of us. They are more or less local and as a rule occur when the air in a given area becomes warmer than the surrounding air. The warm air then rises and expands, cooling as it rises. When sufficient moisture is present we have thunder showers. When moisture is meager, we may get only thunder and lightning. If rain is falling during a thunderstorm, one is comparatively safe from lightning, since the rain disseminates the lightning charges somewhat and conducts the electricity to the earth.

Hail often precedes rain in a thunderstorm, and the question is asked, why do we have hail in the temperate zone during the summer and almost never in winter? Hail is produced when two layers of air, one warm and one frigid, are close together. Save for very extraordinary cases, this can happen only in summer, for in winter the warm layer cannot develop. These two layers of air, being in proximity, produce a wild commotion which causes the water droplets of the cloud to travel violently in a circle. The drops pass alternately through the cold air layer, where they freeze, and through the warm layer where they gather up more moisture to be frozen into ice on their next trip through the cold layer. This process continues until the ice balls grow too heavy to be sustained, when they go tumbling to the earth.

The thunderstorm, so familiar to most people in the temperate zone, is still not our most important rainstorm. The most important rainstorm of the cycle is technically known as the *cyclonic storm*, or *cyclone*. Now, a cyclone is not a tornado, but a large mass of air blowing in a circle around a center of calm. Rarely does a land cyclone cause any disturbance. If you imagine that you are standing in the center of a merry-go-round, with the ponies galloping round you, you will have the picture of the wind movement of a cyclone. As you watch one span of ponies, they gallop past in one direction, but when these chargers are behind you they are going in the opposite direction. Now, if you will think of the entire merry-go-round as several hundred miles in diameter and as moving in a straight line, you will have the replica of a land cyclone in action. A land cyclone usually spells rain, but not always.

Tornadoes are sometimes called concentrated cyclones, an apt name for them. Tornadoes move much as cyclones do, except that the wind whirls at terrific speed. Tornadoes travel in funnel clouds with the small end of the funnel below—and those ghastly funnels can creep up suddenly and cause great destruction before one knows what is happening—unless someone has been watching for them.

And there is that child of the Atlantic Ocean: Carol or Diana or Eva—the *hurricane*. The hurricane is a sea cyclone. In structure it is about the same as the land cyclone, though far more vicious. When the hurricane arrives, the winds in the front rim of the circling storm are blowing in one direction, and when it leaves they are blowing in the opposite direction. The center zone of calm of the hurricane is relatively soothing. Hurricanes cause rainstorms which often are second in volume only to those downpours that originally built our oceans.

In the Oriental tropics this kind of storm is called a *typhoon*. Typhoons normally have their inception in the China Sea. The offshore islands, especially Japan and the Philippines, are regularly and relentlessly bombarded by them during the season of hard rains. The storms gather momentum as they sweep across the turbulent ocean waves, then strike the islands with a twisting force that can be utterly disastrous.

Typhoons seem to have many varieties of destructiveness. I have seen the first winds twist bamboo villages into a corkscrewlike mess and twist jungle trees until they appeared to have been run through a mill. Then come the rearguard winds, racing in the opposite direction, which tear things apart again and send the fragments flying in all directions.

A *cloudburst* is a sudden rainfall that "bursts" down with a resounding splash. The cloud has become so heavily saturated with water before precipitation that it suddenly disintegrates, turning everything loose at once. As a boy, I used to be thrilled when an old Kansas pioneer whom I greatly admired would tell how a cloudburst interfered with the building of his grist mill. The crew had almost completed the dam, which was to run across the creek and provide a pool of water for the huge waterwheel, when a sudden cloudburst up the creek sent the swollen waters pouring down upon them like a rolling sea. The dam was swept away, along with tools and materials. No lives were lost, for the workmen were true water dogs, though several men were carried far down the stream before making it to shore.

In winter, in the United States, when disturbances occur in the upper air, we get a distinctly different type of storm. Indeed, the winter storm occurs in all of North America save for the southern part. It is known for its mixture of snow and sleet and freezing rain and is often called a *blizzard*.

Snow is frozen vapor or frozen mist; and mist is one of the most delicate forms of water in the cycle. It is transformed into geometrical patterns of ice lace when the upper-air temperature drops below freezing.

Sleet, of course, consists of raindrops frozen when they pass through a frigid air stratum on their way down to earth. If you have ever been caught out in a winter storm and been pounded unmercifully by howling winds laden with a combination of snow, rain, and sleet, you need no further definition of a blizzard. Before the advent of the automobile, a North American blizzard could be a terror.

As the Indians used to say, the rain has several children. The common *fog* is a most interesting one. Fog consists of extremely small drops of moisture that are distinct from each other. They are so light they do not settle, and, being carried in an almost saturated atmosphere, they do not readily evaporate. They are tiny raindrops floating in suspension until they are taken up by the sun.

Fog is utilized by some plants as growth moisture. The great conifers of the west coast of the United States can combine the fog droplets into drops of rain. When the fog envelops these firs and pines, the enormous cooling surface of the needles condenses it into raindrops. During a heavy fog this rain pours down through the needles and soaks into the loose soil usually found under pines and firs; the roots take up the moisture in the usual manner.

Hoarfrost is frozen fog. When fog comes into contact with an object whose temperature is below freezing, the fog forms into beautiful lace patterns on the object. Hoarfrost differs from *common frost* in that the latter develops when a saturated atmosphere comes in contact with a frigid object. Some dictionaries call frost frozen dew, but this is a mistake. *Frozen dew* consists of beads of ice that derive from frozen raindrops that were already on the vegetation when the temperature dropped, or from frozen dewdrops. Any down-to-earth farm boy can tell you what frozen dew is. He knows what it means to chase livestock afoot on a brisk winter morning when the vegetation is weighted down with tons of ice beads. Most plants are able to use dew for growth. In semi-desert regions, where dews are heavy, plants drink in great quantities of dew through their leaves, particularly the young leaves. And that is not all: much of the absorbed dew travels through the plant in reverse. It moves down the water channels, oozes out through the roots into the soil, and then is taken up in the normal manner, traveling the transpiration streams up to the leaves. This is the supreme economy of nature at work: water moving up and down the plant at the same time. Careful study in Arizona has revealed that plants may obtain from dew the equivalent of fifteen inches of rain in one season. There is a lesson here for the irrigator, which will be discussed in a later chapter.

Let us now take a journey through primeval soil; through a soil segment of the water cycle not yet wrecked by man. Here, when the rain comes down to earth, every drop falls into a tiny reservoir located behind a little dam, as if the latter were waiting to receive this particular drop. The water then enters the loose, mellow earth.

Drastic changes now begin to occur in that rain water; it starts through a conditioning process. On its way through the top layer of soil the water is enriched in a manner that science cannot explain completely, because so much that takes place cannot be observed. Before the water— Gravity Water it is now called—leaves this upper soil layer, it has taken the first and what is probably the most important step in that road which ultimately leads to quality water in the zone of saturation below.

This first step is that valuable conditioning which the water gets as it moves down through a rich, nature-built soil. After leaving the surface soil and moving on down into the earth, it is further conditioned—if nature's pattern is not interfered with.

The fact that the gravity water now and then courses through undesirable strata, which detract from the quality rather than enhance it, is simply a deviation from nature's quality pattern. The reasons for this are numerous. Excessive minerals—sodium, lime, sulfur, etc.—as we know, give us hard water while a dearth of them provides soft water. Long experience convinces me that nature's balances enter into the building of true quality water, though as yet we are unable to say to what extent this is true. Certainly, for the best quality water a mineral balance is desirable—but scientists are not yet agreed on the norm because of the vast number of factors that enter in.

When I employ the term quality water, I mean water that has, without any deviation, followed nature's water-pattern course: rain water entering a rich, mellow soil where it receives its first conditioning. Exactly what happens to this water as it passes through a rich soil is still much of a mystery. Some important, intangible operations take place, and these operations, which follow Nature's Togetherness Law are indispensable for obtaining Nutritious Quality Water to be stored in the Inland Sea.

As the water moves on down into the lower regions, it gathers desirable minerals and gets rid of the excess bacteria and carbon dioxide which it gathered in the first step, the soil segment, of the quality-water journey. By the time the water reaches the zone of saturation, which is commonly spoken of as the *water table* and which I call the Inland Sea, it has completed the quality-water journey.

What about that rain water we started with? Rain water is merely H_2O, which means that it may be pure, like distilled water, but it is not quality water *until it has traveled nature's water conditioning road*.

The water that remains in the soil segment of the cycle and does not go down to the inland sea is the water that maintains land life. This is virtually the only water that gives land plants and animals their food.

Once, while I was strolling through Central Park in New York City, my attention was drawn to a small clump of weeds which a park attendant had just been watering. From where I stood, the weeds appeared to be old friends from the Southwest growing luxuriantly in that large city. They looked out of place. When I saw how the attendant had flooded the weed patch, I wanted to remind him he was wasting water, that too much water could be as harmful as too little. Of course, I was thinking of that particular kind of water left in the soil after the gravity water had gone on down to the inland sea, that growth water of land plants. I had stooped over to examine the weeds when the park guard came charging at me. I quickly explained that I meant no harm to his little patch of green; that I was a botanist and a soil-and-water specialist and only wanted to inspect the weeds a bit more closely.

When I explained that the weeds would do even better if they were given less water at a time and watered more frequently, the guard lost his belligerency at once and began plying me with questions. He wanted to know how it was possible for valuable plants to get too much water so long as the leaves and stems were not submerged. I tried to explain simply and briefly just what growth water was. "It is a delicate film," I told him, "much like a spider's web."

The guard became silent for a moment. "Like a spider's web!" he finally exclaimed. "And they've been pouring oceans onto my weeds!"

Soon a sizable crowd had gathered, eager to learn more about that spider-web water. I explained that to establish spider-web or growth water it was necessary to put more water onto the soil than plants actually needed—but far less than had been applied. As I moved about the park my audience grew larger. In all my experience I have rarely had an audience so eager for information.

4 Water and the Soil—Capillarity

The Capillary, or Film, water in the soil is the key to the world's food. Only when this film water operates in a soil that closely follows nature's plan of fertility, will it give quality food.

Once I was teaching a high school agriculture class of boys about the capillary movement of water in soil. When I explained that it was not unlike the climb of kerosene up a lamp wick, or the climb of any liquid up a porous cloth, they seemed highly interested.

Two or three weeks after this very practical lesson in capillarity, a man burst into my office without waiting for my secretary to announce him. A glance told me that something was terribly amiss, and it didn't take many seconds for me to learn what.

The man leaned belligerently across my desk. "What

yuh been teachin' our boys here in school?" he shouted in my face. "I know what yer teachin' 'em—yer teachin' 'em to be thieves! Goin' round stealin' people's wine! Borin' a hole through the side of my winery, then hangin' a rag in the vat and snatchin' the wine out like suckin' pop through a straw—"

"Please—just a moment!" I said. "Did you actually see the boys stealing your wine?"

"Caught two of 'em in the act! And I'm goin' to court with it!" And with that my unwelcome visitor whirled and departed.

The news of that wine stealing swept the community. But the justice of the peace, after listening to the wine owner's complaints, refused to hear the case against the boys. Wine might leak from a vat, he concluded, but it could never climb up over the edge of the vat and crawl out a knot hole. The angry owner finally agreed to forget the whole affair if I would agree to punish the boys.

Had I worked for months I could not have found a more efficient scheme for teaching the unlearned the science of water capillarity in soils. People were soon employing the word capillarity almost as intelligently as they used the word water itself. The guilty boys were forced so to master capillarity as to be able to teach its science to the incredulous. And they performed the job well in that section of the dry West.

Man, as a tiller of the soil, rarely stops to realize that his major tillage task is to maintain a soil in which the film water can work at its best, whatever moisture may be available. Above all else, he should center his interest on maintaining the soil segment of the water cycle—as nearly according to nature's pattern as possible.

To comprehend the capillary or film water and its intricate movements and functions in the soil, one should have a good knowledge of the soil itself. A soil built on nature's blueprint is a unique and complete world. It is a dynamic world palpitating with life. Film water is the very heart of this life. This tiny segment of the great *water cycle*—this film of water which envelops the soil particles—is a major factor in the *life cycle*. The life cycle is the progression of life, from form to form. Vigorous life is needed to produce and maintain other life, whether above the soil or within it. Growth is the manifestation of this organic life. To meet all the demands of growth, the combined work of capillary water and a soil with an unbroken fertility chain is required.

The population of such a soil, nature's greatest workshop, is staggering. Leading this array of workers are the billions of microbes, of many kinds, each group performing its own nature-assigned task. There are, as a rule, some microbes that are harmful to growth even in the best of soils; but when conditions are normal, the beneficent microbes usually hold the undesirable ones in check.

Practically all materials which plants demand from the soil must be conditioned by these microbes before the plant can use them in building our foods in the food factory of the leaves.

And those soil organisms lead straight to another soil product which is also a requisite: the soil fiber, commonly known as the organic content. The soil fiber has two special functions along with several other values: it provides a working home for the microbes and it supplies them with food.

Pick up a handful of moist, rich earth, if you have it nearby. Examine it closely. If you live in town and don't make compost, drive out into the country, stop near a patch of woods, and find a spot where nature has developed some forest humus. Don't be afraid to get your hands dirty—it'll probably be the cleanest "dirt" you ever touched. You'll see the broken pieces of leaves and stems and dead rootlets scattered throughout the soil mass. Press the soil gently, and you'll get the sensation of sponginess. It is the soil fiber that produces this spongy effect. You cannot see the microbes, of course, nor the film water, but if the soil is moist you can be sure that both are there. And don't fail to get a whiff of the odor. This is the typical aroma emanating from an active soil workshop, where laborers are operating at top efficiency. This aroma is one of the intangible proofs of quality in soil—a soil that will give you quality food. Plants grown on such soil are able to absorb this quality and pass it on to us.

There are many other inhabitants of the soil's workshop besides the microbes. The various molds or fungi there are among our very best unsung friends. The fungi also require organic matter as a part of their food. These molds give us most of our antibiotics, those guardians of health of which we hear so much these days. In all probability the soil molds have many rich secrets yet to be discovered.

When organic matter decays, the bacteria causing the

decay provide warmth for the workshop; that is, they maintain a uniform temperature in the soil which is essential to best plant growth. In addition, the organic fiber makes the soil porous, guaranteeing correct air circulation. At the same time, it provides those little dams and reservoirs for catching the falling rain—the *insoak* phase of the water cycle. Here we see how closely synchronized are all nature's constructive operations. Quality water and quality food—nature's road leads straight to both.

If your handful of earth is actually virgin soil, you have in your hand a whole universe of living things. The soil in a pot in which you are growing a single plant is, too, a complete universe—if it is as nature would have it. The various microbes perform many different tasks. There are those which bring about decay of organic materials and those which condition minerals for root absorption. Then there are the nitrogen fixers, the bacteria which take free nitrogen from the air within the soil and prepare it for building protein foods in the plant leaves and elsewhere in the plant. And where would the animal kingdom be without protein?

Now a little more about those soil molds or fungi. Some of them work their way right into the roots of plants to obtain food for themselves; but they give the plant more than they take away. A noted English scientist has discovered that certain fungi have the ability to accumulate tiny bits of phosphorus, one of the most important plant-food minerals, and feed this phosphorus right into the plant roots. This fungus-root relationship is so important that many common crops do poorly, or do not grow at all, if the fungi are not present in the soil. I have no doubt but that the tragic depletion of these molds in our mined-out, eroded food-producing soils is one of the main causes of decaying teeth, polio, scurvy, and other troubles which have been attributed to malnutrition.

In the top layer of fertile soil, we find, single-celled green plants—the little protein builders called algae. Some scientists believe that these algae are of little value to the soil, but I do not agree. It might well be difficult to measure their accomplishments, but I'm sure they do far more good than we yet realize. It is safe to assume that anything that gives us protein is closely tied in with nature's plan for sustaining organic life.

Lastly we have the earthworms, nature's efficient tillers. Without earthworms there would probably be much less complete soil on the earth and probably less plant and animal life. Charles Darwin once declared that, if all the animals on the earth were as worthwhile as the earthworms, the world would be a paradise. The earthworms play a vital part in the water cycle, as we shall see.

And there you have it: the world's greatest workshop —a soil built according to the blueprint of nature. It should now be easier to see the place of capillary water in such a soil. Indeed, the capillary or film water enters into every operation of the soil's workshop. If the film water vanishes from the soil or if, on the other hand, the soil becomes flooded, the film is destroyed and all constructive activity of the workshop ceases. Let a severe drought continue over a long period, or gravity water saturate the soil for a few weeks, and you will hear the footsteps of famine. Food crops die; nature's faithful laborers in the workshop also die—or migrate.

The mere fact that water exists in the soil, therefore, does not mean that it is functioning water. The relationship between a soil and its functioning water is an endless wonder to anyone who will pause long enough to study it.

No matter how dry may seem to be the dust on the soil's surface, it still holds a certain small amount of water. We call this hygroscopic water. The sun can rarely get hot enough to draw this hygroscopic water from the soil. Even the dust in our dust storms carries some of it.

Some people experience sheer joy when they stand out in a thunderstorm, watching the rain pour down upon a nature-approved expanse of soil. As they watch that water sink into the earth, they have visions of quality water and quality food; visions of health, happiness, and stability. If such insoak were taking place in all our land, it would mean benefits not obtainable by any other means. Just to envision what is happening to that water as it trickles down through the surface soil is enough to fill one with the desire to spend the rest of one's life repairing the broken soil segments of nature's water cycle on every acre of our cultivated farms. We would then have quality food for everyone, and quality water in every rural section and every city and town in the country. If we could only awaken people everywhere to our basic national need: the need of restoring the insoak to our food-producing soils.

In a dynamic soil workshop, the film water is at its best. To get a clear picture of this film water, we should think of all the soil particles and granules and the pieces of fiber as being enveloped in spider-web films, and all these films connected. Everything that enters the absorbing roots of the plant is first dissolved in the film water. That food-laden film must forever move upward toward the soil's surface from somewhere down below, embracing the rootlets and pouring life-sustaining materials into them.

The majesty of this operation of water in the soil becomes even more impressive when we remember that only the most delicate plant roots can absorb the water film with its nutrients. We call these the root hairs, because they are so tiny. They are short lived and never move from the place where they were formed. Of all the miles of roving roots which a tree, for instance, produces, not one of these roots, except perhaps when it is very young, can absorb any of the water film directly.

Delicate capillary water; fragile, tiny roots which live only a short while—yet the whole plant and animal world, save for those living things that are not tied to the earth, is beholden to them. The only bridge between the plant and the soil is this film of water which envelops the soil particles.

Gravity water on its way down to the inland sea, or water table, leaves the soil supplied with capillary water, but not enough to maintain a continuous flow. For a source of continuous flow we must look deeper into the soil. There, just below the normal root zone of plants, nature in her primitive soils maintains what we may call a temporary water zone. This water-holding zone is built up by the slow downward movement of semidecayed organic stuff. It is vital in nature's complete soil pattern, for it is the source of capillary water during periods of severe drought.

In soils that are tilled, good land management requires

that organic materials, such as green manures, be constantly turned under. In time this fiber will work itself down to the temporary water zone and assure its upkeep. A soil rich in organic matter will produce a crop during a severe drought, whereas land weak in it will fail. This is because the temporary water zone, which lies between the surface soil and the lower soil region, stores an available deposit of water.

As in all her activities, nature follows a pattern in the structure of her water film, a pattern at once static and dynamic. Scientists break the film down into three categories. The first, called *hygroscopic water*, as we have noted, is found in the driest soils and is so tightly held by the dust particles that not even the heat of the sun will draw it out; it cannot be drawn out by heat lower than the boiling point of water. It is completely unavailable to plants and may be considered a permanent part of the soil particles.

The second film may be said to be an outgrowth of the hygroscopic water and is called *inner capillary water.* It may be pictured as the film that develops when a light rain falls on dry soil. It is the hygroscopic water grown thicker and developing, as it were, into a very thin shell. The inner capillary film is held by the soil particles against the pull of gravity. Like the excessively thin hygroscopic water, this inner capillary water is unavailable to plants. It, too, clings to the soil particles and to the hygroscopic water within it.

As the rain continues to fall and the soil receives more and more water, the inner capillary film (visible only under a microscope) becomes thicker and thicker, until it creates a third stage, known as *outer capillary water*. This third film can often be seen by the naked eye, and in this new form the water becomes actively available to plants. Where the hygroscopic and the inner capillary film have clung to the dust, the new outer capillary water fills the space between the dust particles and even the pore spaces themselves if the rain continues. This outer capillary water is the water that moves through the soil, detaching itself from the parent inner film; it is utilized by the plant roots which it enters and nourishes.

We see, then, three stages: hygroscopic water, unavailable for plants, developing into inner capillary water, also unavailable but generating the outer capillary water which carries nutrients and maintains plant life. All three forms of water are alike, in that they are filmlike in form; but only in the thickest stage, the outer capillary film, does the water travel and nourish.

The outer capillary film is at its best immediately following a heavy rain and after the gravity water has gone on its way to become quality water in the inland sea. As long as there is ample water in the temporary water zone, the outer capillary water maintains its thickness and the water will flow uninterruptedly to the plant near the surface of the soil.

The capillary water makes countless bends and turns and folds, enveloping all earth particles and organic fibers. It is at these bends and folds that the film becomes very thick. Here the water "piles up" and is called *angle water*. It is extremely important in agriculture, for here the valuable substances which the plant requires are most highly concentrated. That the capillary water may exist in this manner, as nature requires, it is essential that the tilth and structure of the soil be right.

Sandy soils are very coarse; the particles are so far apart that the film has difficulty in reaching from particle to particle. Clay soils present the opposite condition: the particles are extremely close together and there is not enough space for a thick water film. In both cases the soil fiber, organic matter, becomes the balancer, and the farmer who refuses to recognize this is certain to be the loser. In sandy soils the fiber builds bridges between the large particles. In clays it pushes the particles apart so that the capillary film can establish itself.

The tiny root hairs are far from being the end of the journey which the capillary water must travel. There is still the mysterious climb of the water up the channels of the plant to the leaves—one of the most amazing phenomena of nature. Imagine what that climb must involve in a towering cypress! When the capillary water leaves the soil, loaded with its burden of food materials, it enters a new world and its functions change completely. Now it becomes *plant water*, nature's nutritious, quality water number two. The bamboo water mentioned in the first chapter is this quality water number two.

5 Water and the Plant

Have you ever sat down in front of a vigorous, growing plant and wondered what was actually going on inside it? For the inquisitive, there is ground for profound thought in just a few minutes of such contemplation. It matters little whether it be a bean or cornstalk; a wheat culm or a creeping pumpkin vine; a rose or a majestic oak. Fundamentally the growth operations will be the same: invisible water flowing up the water channels, invisible water in every living tissue, water employed to build the basic food in the leaf, water carrying this manufactured food to all parts of the plant either for growth or storage, the water transpiring in enormous volumes from the leaf surface, thus cooling the air and providing comfort for the animal world. Water is active everywhere in the plant and actually makes up nearly all the plant's volume, yet you don't see a drop of it.

Supposing we take a mental journey through this water-filled plant, beginning with that marvelous bridge which connects the plant with the soil. But before we start that intriguing journey, we must reveal a secret about plant roots. On our mental journey through the soil we followed the capillary-water film as it wended its way from the temporary water reservoir which, in a correct soil, is located just below the normal root zone of crops, and up through the soil particles on its way to the soil's surface. The water film was loaded with food materials in solution, ready to be taken up by the plant's tiny absorbing rootlets. While it is true that the capillary movement of water through the soil is extremely important, it has been recognized for some time that plants prefer to go after their water and food rather than wait for the water and food to come to them. Roots are voracious rovers and they will pry into the most impossible places for water and food materials. Give a root a very small crevice in a huge rock and it will persist in its efforts until it has finally split the boulder, often breaking the rock to bits.

At times land plants go amazing distances to forage for water. I came upon an excellent illustration of this in a western state. It was in a section of the state where land was expensive and water for irrigation even more so. Two farmers owned farms on opposite sides of a traveled road. One was a dairyman, whose chief crop was alfalfa; the other was a fruit grower who specialized in high-quality commercial peaches.

One day, as I was driving along the road, the dairy farmer signaled for me to stop. He wanted me to accompany him to his irrigation reservoir, which was near the road, and see what he had found. Some new weed needing identification, I thought. But it was something else. He pointed accusingly across the road at his neighbor's peach trees. Their roots, he said, had crept under the road and were robbing him of his irrigation water.

Being unfamiliar with the drinking habits of land plants, the dairy farmer had good reason for looking upon the peach trees as water thieves. The peach-tree roots were protruding into the reservoir, and it was natural to conclude that they were really drinking the water. The trees in the first two rows, directly across from the reservoir, revealed their guilt conspicuously. All the trees in the orchard were well cared for, but those particular trees were larger and more vigorous than the rest. I did my best to make the dairy farmer understand that those visible peach roots were mostly fakes; that they were actually not drinking much water. But I wasn't convincing him. Seeing was believing—and wasn't it the business of roots to drink in water?

Those roots were not stealing his water *directly*, though I knew very well what was taking place: there was a lateral capillary movement of the water from the earth reservoir, no doubt extending out for several feet. From this capillary area the peach trees were obtaining their water in the proper manner of land plants. As they drank this film water, capillarity kept more water moving in.

As we follow the capillary water from the soil and on into the plant, we encounter some vital operations that are still deeply submerged in theory. Just how does that water film get into the root hair? And, once the water is inside the rootlet, loaded down with rich materials from the soil's workshop, how does it climb to the highest leaves of a towering tree?

To begin with, we must remember that the only openings of the plant are found in the leaves. That is, practically the only openings. There are no openings in the roots. Nevertheless, the film water does get into the rootlet. But science cannot tell us too much about the manner in which it does this. Another important fact is that not all the substances which the food factory requires from the soil travel up those rivers of water, though they all seem to enter the root hair in about the same way. Some of the soil substances move up the plant by what we call *diffusion;* that is, by moving up slowly from cell to cell. How? Just more theory. But for the moment we shall concern ourselves with the materials that go up with the water in what the botanists call the *transpiration* streams.

It is impossible to overemphasize the stupendous importance of that bridge which spans the gulf lying between the plant and the soil. Oddly, this is a moving bridge. The entire bridge, or water film, moves with its burden right on across the gulf and into the root hair. This seems to be about what takes place: root hairs, because they are continuously drained of their contents by the passing of nutrients to other parts of the plant, are always eager to receive fresh supplies from the water film and its contents. As the root hair keeps emptying itself, it exercises in the process a kind of suction effect on the water film. And it is believed that the root hair must be at least partly empty before any substance from outside can pour through it to those transpiration streams. Scientifically this is called *osmotic action*, or *osmosis*, and at the present time it is the most logical theory we have. In the laboratory, osmosis is commonly demonstrated as follows: a membraneous bag, containing sugar water and having a tube attached to it, is placed in a vessel of pure water. Soon the liquid rises in the tube, showing that the pure water is "oozing" through the membrane, but the sugar water, being denser, cannot ooze out. The sum total of this process is called osmosis.

Immediately the water film is inside the plant, it loses its identity; it is now a part of a tiny river of water—bound on a long journey up to nature's only food factory. If the plant happens to be a giant oak, that journey will indeed be a long one. There are thousands of these little rivers, even inside an ordinary plant stem. Each river has its own root station in the soil; each one starts from a capillary bridge.

Just get the picture: the stem of any living green plant a vast realm of flowing rivers!

A wilted plant is an interesting study. It illustrates how vitally important all those flowing rivers in the plant are. A wilted plant is one whose water flow through the tissues has ceased. In other words, it's a plant that has lost its turgidity. A turgid plant is one bulging with water; one whose transpiration streams are bank full. When plant tissues are not saturated with water, it means that death is creeping pretty close. The same water law operates in animals. Let the water content drop below a certain point and the functioning of all organs stops, both in plants and in animals.

Every plant is composed of minute sections called cells. Each plant cell is complete and distinct, yet all cells must work together, and water is the agent which sees that they work together efficiently. Every newly formed plant cell is composed largely of protoplasm and, save for the cell wall, is not vastly different from the first single-celled plants produced in the sea at the beginning of organic life. Botanists tell us the original one-celled plants contained chiefly protoplasm and a nucleus or "heart." All new plant cells when viewed under the microscope consist mostly of protoplasm and a nucleus. Water moves through and around all these cells, carrying stuff in and carrying it out, in various and sundry ways keeping the plant machinery working.

But more about those transpiration streams—and the perpetual question: what maintains their upward flow against the relentless pull of gravity? How does this water reach the highest leaves of a tall tree? We have an abundance of plausible theories, but that is all. There are, no doubt, several forces involved, each probably having a share in making that long climb possible, but the most reasonable seems to be the transpiration theory.

The *transpiration theory* is this: As water transpires or breathes out from the leaves, more water is "drawn" up to take its place. We need to keep in mind that the interior of the plant is somewhat like a vacuum which permits the water molecules to hang together tenaciously. But there is a knotty joker in this transpiration theory. It may work with trees that don't shed their leaves, but what moves the water up in the spring in trees that have no leaves at that period? Or in the tropics, where the transpiration from leaves is extremely meager for much of the year? Where does the water come from that awakens the buds and starts spring growth? True, there is always some water in the dormant bud, but is there enough to develop the leaf?

A plant scientist and I were once sitting under a tree in General Grant Park in California, feasting our eyes on the world's largest tree, the General Grant. The shade tree under which we were sitting was several feet in diameter and had an extensive spread. But the majesty of the great General dwarfed everything around it: two hundred and sixty feet high, with a diameter of more than forty feet. We had been discussing that upward flow of the plant rivers; the mystery of those transpiration rivers and our pathetic ignorance of it all.

"If that monarch does nothing else, it goes a long way in revealing how insignificant we humans are," my friend said, turning to me. "Imagine the amount of water transpiring from that enormous leaf surface up there! How does all that water climb so high?"

Maybe the great tree knows; we do not!

We cannot pass from this profound demonstration by nature, of which we know so little, without calling attention to the *surface-tension theory*. Surface tension means the tendency of a liquid surface to contract and become as small as possible. According to this theory, when the moisture in the dormant bud becomes warm in the spring and starts to transpire into the air, the moisture in the stem moves upward, because of the contraction caused by the surface tension pull, to fill the tiny vacuum caused by the start of transpiration—and thus the transpiration rivers start their flow. They continue to flow until the leaves fall in autumn and the new buds are put to sleep within their winter blankets. The transpiration theory and surface-tension theory are practically the same; mostly they represent a difference in nomenclature.

Have you ever noticed that some plants bleed freely in the spring before the leaves are developed? Grape vines often will really pour water from a cut. It's the bleeding in sugar-maple trees which gives us our maple syrup. Plant physiologists say that the bleeding is caused by a terrific pressure of some kind within the roots which develops immediately spring temperature arrives. As soon as the leaves appear, the wound heals and the bleeding stops, though the root pressure, at least to a degree, likely continues right on through the summer and serves as one of the powers that keep the transpiration streams flowing.

Leaving our transpiration rivers for a moment, let us now consider nature's only food factory, the leaf. Since the first arrival of green plants on the earth, green foliage has been manufacturing all food for plants and animals alike; yet the leaf itself is simple in structure. There are two outer membraneous coverings, the upper and the lower, which are tough and serve as protectors of the food factory which is between them. In the case of land plants, almost all the plant's openings, called stomata (from a Greek word meaning "tongues"), are located in the lower surface of the leaf. Most water plants have the stomata on the upper surface.

Nature carefully guards against any interference with her food factory inside the leaf. This leaf interior is made up mostly of postlike strengthening cells and a meshwork of irregular cells in which are located little green bodies called *chloroplasts*. The chloroplasts play a vital part in the food processing. Chlorophyll (the sum total of all the chloroplasts), sunlight, carbon-dioxide gas, water—all working together—combine in a process called *photosynthesis*. Though we know more about photosynthesis than we know about the powers that brought those materials from the soil's workshop up to the food factory, there still is much concerning the activities that take place in the food factory that science is not too sure about.

However, we do know a fair amount about some of them. Let's start with sugar. In the manufacture of sugar, our foundation food, water plays a major role in two ways: it assists mechanically in that process called photosynthesis, in that it moves materials about; and the water forms part of the sugar molecule itself. In forming the sugar molecule the water is destroyed. This is what happens: water (H_2O) and carbon-dioxide gas (CO_2), the latter entering the leaf both from the air and in the water which comes up in the transpiration streams, are broken down; their several elements—hydrogen, oxygen, and carbon—combine to form our basic sugar ($C_6H_{12}O_6$) and free oxygen. The motive power here is sunlight. Without sunlight there is no food-making activity.

Next, organic substances called enzymes take the sugar molecule and work it over—and you have starch. Fat is made in the same way. Protein, which is often called the supreme food, is built by the addition of another gas, nitrogen. The nitrogen comes from the air but reaches the leaf via the transpiration streams which flow up from the soil. The nitrogen is usually accompanied by sulfur. Some scientists say that other minerals, particularly phosphorus, join the food molecule when the protein is formed.

There are many kinds of protein, and the protein molecule carries with it most of our mineral foods as well as the less common food ingredients. Protein is really the dictator of organic life.

The building of our foods is only the first step; these foods must now be transported throughout the plant, either to be used immediately in growth and propagation or to be stored for future generations. It is largely this stored food which supports animals and man. Sugars, fats, starches, proteins with their accompanying nutrients—we need them as much as the plant does.

And now to the end of our journey and out through almost the only doors in the plant: out through those stomata in the lower surface of the leaf. After depositing their burdens in the food factory, the transpiration rivers pour out through the leaf doors, and the water is immediately changed to vapor. All this vapor was at one time just a water film—or countless films—wrapped around the soil particles in the soil's workshop below, waiting to enter the plant through the delicate root hairs.

Have you ever driven along the highway in summer, with the wind blowing in your face from a dry, parched area, and suddenly come to a green field and felt the cool air? The transpiration of water from plants always has that cooling effect. Changing the transpiration water into vapor uses up a lot of heat, and the surrounding air is cooled off in the process. Pure oxygen is always coming out of those leaf doors also, the oxygen that was left over from the building of that sugar molecule in the food factory. In large measure it is this air, rich in moisture and free oxygen, that makes the shade under trees so delightful as the heat of the day bears down.

Green plants in a livingroom are wonderful purifiers. They take in and utilize the gas given off by humans (CO_2) and in turn give back pure oxygen and moisture, which together maintain a wholesome balance. Such plants in a sick room, on occasions, may be worth more than a doctor's prescription, particularly during a convalescing period, when abundant oxygen is needed for strength building.

The amount of water needed to keep that food factory operating is almost beyond our conception. Has it ever occurred to you, when sitting down to a sumptuous meal, just how much water was required for the production of that meal? To grow one ear of sweet corn on ordinary soil requires around seventy five gallons of water. One slice of bread calls for many, many gallons. A juicy steak, counting the amount of water needed to grow the feed for the animal plus the amount of water the animal consumes during its life—well, in that steak there is involved a sizable river.

The efficiency of the soil's workshop governs very definitely the amount of water needed by the plant. The poorer the soil the more water is needed to provide a sufficiency of food materials to keep the food factory operating. Very little water, in comparison, is needed for the actual building of the food molecule. It's those transpiration rivers that call for the huge amount of water. After all, in this instance the chief mission of the water is as a carrier. Since the plant needs so much food-making material, if the soil is rich the water coming from that soil will also be "rich"—and a much smaller volume will take care of the plant's needs than where the soil is poor.

Civilized man can learn from the savage. During my extensive travels among primitive and semiprimitive tribes, I was constantly amazed at their uncanny understanding of the aspects of nature with which they were obliged to live intimately. This comprehension of nature was particularly manifest in knowledge of wild plants.

It took the wild man to bring home to me the enormous worth of *plant water,* the value to animal well-being of the water in those transpiration streams which we have just discussed. The savage has proved the worth of this plant water as a medicine for his ills and has found it to be a preventative of some of his worst jungle maladies. Of course, the primitive man classifies his plants most efficiently, even though the reasons he will give you for his classifications are often quaint. These people will stagger you with their practical knowledge of healing. I have seen festering sores that would baffle the keenest mind of the white medicine man beautifully healed in a short time by the *correct* application of plant water to the wound.

The natives' utilization of plant water as food was a never-ending wonder to me. Different kinds of plants, of course, have their own specific values. Some plants give special strength when the juice is squeezed out and taken raw. (If you win the wise one's confidence he will show you just how to extract the juice. It's an art.) Then there are plants that have to be stewed if the water is to give best results. There are particular plants whose juice, when diluted with other water, is superb as a medium in which to cook other foods, expecially meats. Many times I have eaten food cooked in this manner and found it delicious beyond description. Savor and aroma, also, spoke highly for the food's nutritive worth.

Nature's Quality Water Number Two—and it took a savage to bring it home to me—is plant water. Our fore-parents were aware of the value of their potherbs in a well-rounded diet, but in our mechanical age we have prac-tically lost connection with the simple laws of nature in-volved. Nature is no respecter of persons, be one savage or civilized. Therefore, I offer this advice: give plant water—water from choice potherbs (greens) grown on a nature-approved soil—a permanent place in the diet, and the gen-eral health of our country will noticeably improve. This quality water number two, according to nature's scheme of things, should have a permanent place in our diet. The wild man has proved it to be an indispensable health factor.

Once I carried on a conversation, through my inter-preter, with a wizened old savage. He was busily engaged in squeezing the juice from a succulent plant and gulping the juice down. We were trying to find out about how old the man was. Through his remembrance of past events, we determined that he was somewhere around one hundred and forty. His teeth were gone, but not because of disease or decay. Like all such people, he had worn them out through constantly biting hard objects.

I asked him to tell me something about that plant water he seemed to relish. He appeared bewildered for a moment; presently he looked at me with squinting eyes. "To keep well and live long one must eat good food," he explained; "and the water inside the plants always satisfies."

Quality water number one, the savage drinks from his springs whenever he can reach them; quality water number two he drinks from his green plants—and on the whole enjoys a long, healthy existence.

6 Water and the Animal—The Inland Sea

The wild beast is water wise. Much has been written about the mysterious water holes of the jungles where the wild things quench their thirst. It is generally believed by the people in those lands that these drinking holes are frequented by the wildlife because of the peculiar quality of the water the holes contain. This water might well have a special nutritive value because of the fact that it comes directly from springs or from underground seepage. Certainly these frequently sought drinking holes contain water as nature intends it for land-animal consumption.

This is not to say that wild animals do not drink from other pools and from flowing streams. Naturally they do, but this seems to be emergency drinking; drinking when fear dominates. Where conditions are normal, many species of wild beasts travel long distances to drink at certain springs; to reach these, they often cross streams of clear water.

Experienced jungle hunters are aware of the truce that appears to exist among blood-spilling beasts around these choice water holes. I have explored many of these holes, in tropical jungles and in mountainous regions of the temperate zone. In both zones wild animals clearly relish this choice water. Beaten paths radiate from these springs like the spokes of a giant wheel.

Wild animals do not seek these springs and special holes because they offer less danger. In the mountains, the springs are generally located in dead-end canyons or among huge boulders where enemies can easily lie in wait. Almost the same situation obtains in tropical jungles. I know this to be a fact because I have personally observed it in several parts of the world.

What is even more revealing is that most wildlife will insist on drinking at the spring itself rather than from the clear pools below the spring, even though these pools must also contain excellent water. One is forced to wonder if spring water, where it first emerges from the earth, carries a special quality still unknown to us. It is possible that the lower animal, ever instinctively wise to nature's laws, is able to measure water quality that is still beyond the perception of civilized man.

We tread on a vast ocean of water: Nature's Inland Sea. Let us now recall that when nature brought plant and animal protoplasm onto the land from those long-ago oceans, through her water cycle she provided the means of maintaining the water content of the protoplasm. So far, our treatment of the water cycle has included about every type of activity: calm and storm, heat and cold, and related forces. Now we come to the segment of the cycle which is enveloped largely in the unknown, the inland sea. It is to the inland sea that nature expects us to go for our nutritious quality water. It is the only water that meets all the requirements of land-animal existence completely. (Land plants do not require this water from the deep zone of saturation, as we have already learned, though they will thrive on it as long as it is supplied to them in a capillary form.)

Geologists are able to interpret to a considerable degree the composition of our inland sea, but most of what we know about that water world is till wrapped in theory. However, interpreting the unknown by what is known, geologists have given us a glimpse of the inland sea that is probably not far from the complete picture.

A vast water world shrouded in the blackest of darkness! But we must not think of our inland sea as we think of the Atlantic or the Caribbean. It's a very different kind of sea. We should think of it as a "sea of saturation". When we think of this great volume of underground water, two words take on more than ordinary meaning. These two words are *Saturation* and *Pore*, or pore space. Pores are the spaces found between material particles, like the air spaces in sand and gravel. In our inland sea, pore space can refer to huge caverns, since interspaces of great size no doubt exist among the boulders that probably, here and there, form mountainlike masses. It's not too difficult to imagine the floor of our inland sea as being made up of mountains and valleys much like the floors of the Atlantic and Pacific. Yet the inland sea differs from all external water bodies in that the water is carried in the pore spaces much as water is carried in a sponge.

Let us try to picture in our minds an inland sea with just such a mountainous floor and with all the open spaces among the solid materials filled with nutritious, quality water. Perhaps in one place we have broad sweeps of water-saturated sand; in another, cubic miles of coarse gravel, every tiny interspace filled with water. Here and there, no doubt, are acres of clay whose pores are very small. Though these pores are also filled, the water is not easily released. Wells depending on such clay stratum for their water are likely to be weak. But picture those large, dark caverns among the boulders; pores as large as caves and all filled with crystal water! Then imagine a particularly fine spring flowing above ground from such a water source; or a domestic well tapping it. There are, of course, such wells and springs, and many of us, at some period in our lives, have been familiar with them, though probably never stopping to wonder about that water's source. A creek that flows abundantly during a long drought, or a well that maintains a steady level during a similar period, quite possibly is supplied by such a stratum.

The upper surface of our inland sea, commonly spoken of as the *water table*, is quite unstable. At times the table rises almost to the earth's surface; again, it may drop to great depths. Geologists say that the greatest depth of the water table is theoretically about ten miles, though practically it is seldom more than half a mile.

Right at this point, man encounters the weakness or efficiency of that storage of quality water. The inland sea is sustained entirely by the gravity water that passes down through the soil segment of the cycle. *Erosion* is the fiend that depletes our quality water, for the runoff on eroded land, except in very limited amounts, does not enter the soil. Instead, it creates floods that finally carry it to the sea; or it pours into domestic reservoirs, as erosion slush, to be drugged and made "safe" for human consumption. In direct proportion to man's wreckage of the insoak conditions of the soil segment of the cycle, in that proportion is he choosing to drink erosion slush rather than quality water. And, even more, he is bleeding the inland sea; driving the zone of saturation farther and farther beyond his reach. Wells in many sections of our country that once stood high and provided an abundance of quality water now supply only a trickle. The inland sea in many regions is drying up, because of man's ignorance and selfishness. Erosion slush is taking over as the only water supply for the home in most towns and cities—with the inevitable consequences: health disturbances of several sorts which may be charged incorrectly to other causes. One of the most conspicuous among these is tooth decay among the younger generation. Many dentists will tell you that low-quality food and low-quality water are wrecking the teeth of youth.

Now and then there exists, several feet below the soil's surface, an impenetrable layer of clay which checks the downward movement of gravity water, even when the soil segment of the water cycle is functioning efficiently. This brings about what is called a *perched water zone*. What people in rural areas often speak of as wet-weather wells or springs are supplied by this perched water. In most instances perched water will not carry through a drought, and springs at that time go dry or nearly so. Often, however, the volume of this water holds up quite steadily in springs and wells, though the supply is seldom extensive. To play safe, the well should be dug, or drilled, through the impervious or hardpan layer, to the permanent zone of saturation below.

Our inland sea differs from the external oceans and lakes in one other vital respect. The inland sea is a shifting body of water, continually flowing, though at a snail's pace. Were it not for this continuous changing of this sea of darkness, the saturation zone below large areas of impermeable material would be waterless. Artesian reservoirs are always found below extensive impervious layers. The water source of an artesian well is likely to be far from the well itself.

The movement of the inland sea may also prove disastrous. Let us picture a community of excellent farms, whose people are industrious and take special pride in their wells of abundant, quality water. Some miles away is a small industrial center which has caught the eyes of one or two manufacturing concerns. Large factories are built which call for great quantities of water. Wells are drilled and machine pumps set in motion. Water begins to pour from the inland sea. Then, that thriving farm community sees its wells start going down, a condition that is inevitable, since both communities are drawing from the same zone of saturation. Although it may have taken centuries to fill that water-bearing stratum or *aquifer*, the water now may be pulled down in the matter of months to the point where that thriving farm community finds itself in despair—and probably not able to do a thing about it.

A glaring example of the bleeding of an aquifer occurred many years ago in the San Joaquin Valley of California. The Valley, at that time, rested upon perhaps the largest saturation zone of quality water in the United States. Then came the demand for small, intensive farms in what was promising to be the garden spot of America. Colonization companies saw their bonanza and moved in. "Ten acres and independence" became their slogan. Unscrupulous real-estate activities for a long time went unchecked. I know, for I was the agriculturist for one of the largest companies in the Valley. This company was basically honest, but it had competitors who were far less so. Consequently, irrigation wells became as numerous as toadstools on a meadow. In a short time I saw the handwriting clear across the land.

But the land salesmen laughed at me. "Look at those mountains of snow on the Sierras and Coast Range!" they'd say. "No danger of the old San Joaquin Valley going dry!" They refused to recognize the facts about those annual mountains of snow. In the first place, if every drop of that snow water had gone into the ground, there still wouldn't have been enough water each season to replenish what was taken out of the zone by the large number of wells. In the second place, overgrazing in the far reaches of the mountains was destroying the insoak conditions there, and the snow water, instead of going into the earth, was roaring down the tributaries of the San Joaquin River; the San Joaquin carried it to the sea.

In the end, the San Joaquin Valley became a land of contrasts: torn by destructive floods, yet screaming for irrigation water. No matter what may be done to promote large-scale ditch irrigation in the San Joaquin Valley, it is unlikely that that marvelous sea of quality water can ever be returned to its original status.

It has been found practical, by means of ditch irrigation, for man to build an inland sea where little or no saturation existed before. Some arid regions, believed worthless, can now be made habitable. This has already taken place in some parts of the West. However, filling a dry saturation zone with water by means of ditch irrigation on the surface is not always feasible, since the rock and sand formations below are sometimes such that they lose the water as fast as it percolates into them. Much might be gained by having a complete geological survey made of arid districts in order to locate those which give special promise. Certainly a region which could be shown, by survey, to possess an ideal saturation zone would be far more valuable, for development, than one in which it was known that the community, no matter how great the insoak might be, would be sitting on a dry saturation zone.

Periodically, across the years, the question arises of tapping the inland seas beneath the world's deserts. Watering and populating the Sahara has long been a French dream. Possibly all important regions of the Great Desert have been geologically surveyed. Water has been reported to be generally abundant, though at varying depths. The fact that oases appear here and there, with water wells of good quality, indicates what might be expected over larger areas. And the Sahara soils are not greatly different from the run of desert soils: rich in minerals quickly available. With an ample water supply and the addition of organic matter, it might be possible to turn a large portion of the Sahara into fertile land.

But to plunge into such a venture without taking into account the exact science involved in nature's water cycle could lead to dire consequences. As California and several other regions have had to learn, nature created the water cycle for a particular purpose, or series of purposes. Equally important, she designed it to operate according to a set pattern. Granted that there is a vast inland sea beneath the Sahara, with the water located at economical depths below the earth's surface, the question arises: whence came that ocean of underground water? Certainly not through direct percolation from above. Rains are too sparse in all parts of the Sahara to provide any appreciable amount of water for an inland sea of saturation. This means that the underground flow has come to its present position through the slow movement of the inland sea itself. It must also mean that water has been accumulating probably over millennia and millennia. Indeed, in building up whatever sea there is beneath the Sahara, the accumulation has been taking place so slowly that the annual addition to the zone of saturation has been extremely meager. Compare that slow build-up of the inland sea with the staggering volume of water that would have to be drawn out were the land turned to cultivation. Drops against billions of gallons.

Great deserts exist for reasons, some of which are not easy for man to comprehend. Before attempting to transform a barren waste, which is not uncommonly possible, it is always wise to ask: does nature approve?

What limited knowledge we have of the inland sea is enough to whet our desire to learn more about it. Geologists, every so often, give us a new glimpse of that region that sends our imagination exploring. The waters deep in the earth include some odd specimens that fill us with wild conjectures. Far below even the deepest portions of the inland sea, for example, there is a freak occurrence that springs from one of the chemical ingredients of the buried rocks. It is a stream of salt water that breaks away from the sheltering boulders and goes gallivanting around like a spirited youngster. It is in fact called *juvenile water*, because its age probably doesn't exceed several millennia. This juvenile water, now and then through seepage, wanders into hot regions and is hurled out like lava from a volcano, or is gushed out as part of a geyser. The history of this juvenile water would probably be as thrilling as the beginning of the earth itself.

Connate water is another odd form found deep in the earth. It is located is isolated pools, as is petroleum. In prehistoric times, when the earth was still young and going through drastic transformations, this connate water was trapped and isolated into its pools. There it has remained, hidden in darkness, for centuries beyond number. Connate water now and then causes trouble during drilling for oil. That is, trouble deep down in the earth.

Occasionally the pools of this natural water are rich in minerals, but the expense of salvaging is seldom warranted because the pools are buried so far below the earth's surface.

The more one dwells on the immeasurable value of our inland sea to all animal life and to man in particular, the more one is sickened by the wreckage of so large a portion of our earth's surface. Every acre mutilated by erosion means a bleeding of the inland sea.

Water conservation and soil conservation are inseparable. For all the majesty and mystery of our inland sea, it is still at the mercy of man. We cannot remind ourselves too often that the replenishment of this zone of saturation depends on the gravity water that pours down through the soil. And we must repeat: erosion slush, beyond a very limited extent, does not enter the soil to assist in maintaining that storehouse of nature's quality water. This consideration leads us to the soil segment of the water cycle; to those miniature dams and reservoirs which fulfill nature's insoak pattern. So, when our wells start going down and our springs dry up, let us remember that one, perhaps two, things are happening: erosion has destroyed nature's insoak pattern; the saturation zone is being drained more rapidly than it is being refilled.

Possibly the early Pennsylvania Dutch settlers were more sensitive to water quality than any of the pioneers. A superior domestic well was as indispensable as the Bible and a hominy kettle. Dutch wells were always carefully located and dug and walled according to a set plan that had come with the pioneers across the ocean and was grisly with age. And a well without an oaken bucket would no more have been acceptable than would have been a well dug without the approval of the community water witch.

Our Dutch well in the settlement near Abilene, Kansas, comes back to me vividly. My father would have nothing but a replica of the Pennsylvania well of his forefathers. This meant a well large and deep and walled with limestone blocks. Thick walls were essential to maintain a uniform temperature throughout the year. And of course there was the mossy, oaken, iron-bound bucket!

A quality well or lush spring: the first, man's faucet to the inland sea of quality water; the second, nature's outlet for that same quality water; the water which she provided for us when she moved life onto the land in the long ago. But when we refuse to obey nature's laws of the cycle, water strikes back by giving us too much water in the form of erosion slush, which leads to destructive floods; or too little water, which may result in dust storms and devastating droughts.

In our own country and in several other parts of the world, one of the most illogical phases of land management to be found is the drainage of fresh-water swamps. The swamp is a vital link in nature's water balance. Few stop to realize that whenever one of these swamps is drained, the water table or inland sea is bound to be dangerously lowered. This lowering will probably occur in some thriving community—and not infrequently a community far from the swamp. So, whenever swamp drainage is contemplated, the community or organization attempting the operation should first ask the question: what effect will it have on surrounding neighborhoods?

The building of great numbers of farm ponds which is being done throughout the country is certain to result in national benefits. Where swamp drainage weakens the inland sea, every farm pond strengthens it. Indeed, great numbers of deep farm ponds dotting the land, along with small upstream lakes, will do far more to stabilize our national water dilemma than will the large, expensive reservoirs now advocated by so many, no matter how numerous the latter may be. The ponds and upstream reservoirs catch the water and prevent erosion, something the large downstream "lakes" cannot do. We like to envision the day when the home farm will be revived and each farm contain ponds of sufficient depth to provide water for irrigation where needed. Ponds can fill a vital need in the production of adequate quality food instead of the less desirable foods now being mass produced in great surpluses.

7 The Road Back

Water conservation, as viewed by two segments of the general public, falls into two distinct and largely unrelated categories: the first is on a vast scale, glamorous, but in the long run must be considered as temporary. The second is far less arresting in appearance, but is logical and builds for permanence.

In the first instance the aim is to catch and corral the erosion slush, with its countless tons of sediment scraped from once-productive fields that are still being unmercifully ravaged. The second category has for its aim the healing of the sore at its source by repairing the soil segment of the water cycle. There is no glamor in this; just national salvation through improved health via quality water and quality food. This is the view that spells conservation in the minds of the conservation organizations of our country.

And it spells true conservation in the mind of this author. But we can't repair a house that is on fire. We've got to put the fire out first. We have to stop the tragic runoff from our lands and thus prevent even more serious floods. Besides, this silt-laden runoff is water—of a sort—and our modern way of life demands water and more water: for machines and for creating power to run the machines.

Every advance in civilization means a greater use of water. When we exchanged the water bucket in the house for the faucet, and the washtub for the bathtub and shower, we increased the demand for water by uncountable millions of gallons. And this is a mere trickle compared with the call for water in industry. The watering trough on the street was the chief water interest in the business district sixty years ago, but today oceans are required for the many types of industry and manufacturing. So the large reservoir hears the call and moves in.

There is the agricultural angle, too. Our agriculture seems to pass periodically through some evolutionary change. We are on the threshhold of a change today which may lead to a more intensive, better type of farming so far as production of food crops is concerned. The evolution consists of the introduction of irrigation practices in many regions to counter the normally dry periods in summer and to guarantee crops during prolonged droughts. This new agriculture calls for great volumes of water where little or none was called for before.

Most of this irrigation should come from farm ponds especially constructed for the purpose. But because such ponds are not always feasible, the impounding of enormous volumes of runoff in reservoirs to control floods can also make another important contribution by providing water for land that might otherwise be of little value for the growing of crops. There is hope that, with this assurance of irrigation, there will be an incentive to build up poor land according to nature's pattern—which would in turn give back that high-quality, nutritious food which is so desperately needed.

But even if great reservoirs had no other value, their hydroelectric possibilities alone would warrant their existence—so long as they did not submerge large areas of valuable land and so become implements of destruction. As industry continues to grow, electrical needs inevitably increase. And the electrical requirements of private houses are vastly greater than they were even a few years ago. Rural houses today have many electrical needs.

The day of electricity is here, and the big reservoir, with its hydroelectric power potential, must be accepted.

But then the question comes up, what about the future of those hydroelectric reservoirs? You cannot hope to pour countless tons of sediment into a reservoir year after year and expect the reservoir to store water indefinitely. It must ultimately fill with mud. What becomes of water storage then? Do you build another dam and another lake somewhere near, to replace the one that has been filled? To this, a dim voice in the distance seems to be saying: "Perhaps, by then, atomic power will be ready to take over."

On the other hand, by rebuilding the soil segment of the water cycle, we build for posterity. To repair that segment, however, we have to control erosion. True conservation *means* erosion control. Consequently, we are faced with this challenge: granted the values of the large reservoir, do

they outrank the human need for quality water? Or for
health-carrying quality food? (Remember, that as we repair the soil's workshop, the soil segment of the water
cycle, we establish desirable insoak and put quality into our
food-producing soils as well. Soil conservation and water
conservation are synonymous!)

So long as there *is* runaway slush, it is extremely important that we capture and control every drop of it. Our
greatest need right now is to obtain quality water for sustaining man himself, and there is only one source of that
quality water: the inland sea, the zone of saturation beneath our feet. And the only way we can repair the inland
sea is to catch the rain and send it on its conditioning journey down through the earth. That is an unbreakable law in
nature's water pattern. And that is why, when funds are
being appropriated to enable the building of large structures for corralling muddy water, thought should be given
to the kind of conservation that will lead to nutritious quality water needed to sustain health in man himself.

While we are taking care of the machine it is certainly
not wise to neglect the mechanic. Spending millions, even
billions, to construct large reservoirs, only to starve the
permanent work of soil conservation and the replenishment
of quality water, certainly is weak logic.

To comprehend fully our complete relationship to water, we need always to think of water as one of nature's
basic foods. And here we *must* repeat: there is but one
road to nutritious water, and it is the insoak road through
the soil segment of the water cycle.

Repairing ravaged land calls for careful planning, and
the logical starting point is at the individual farm. The late

Louis Bromfield liked to tell how the rebuilding of the sponge in his soils at Malabar Farm brought back the springs in the draws, springs that had been dry for many decades. It was possible to do this even though some neighboring farmers were not carrying on the same constructive operations. A farmer, then, can improve the saturation zone below his own land when his neighbors do not choose to do the same. It is true that the inland sea is constantly but slowly shifting, but it is also true that gravity water pouring down from above maintains considerable stability in the saturation zone in a given area.

In restoring insoak, green manures will ever be the chief working factors in the operation. But merely turning under one or two crops will not repair the soil's sponge structure. In most instances, many crops will be needed. Furthermore, achieving a spongy soil through the addition of organic materials does not necessarily mean that the soil has regained its natural spongy structure. To be sure, this coarse "temporary sponge" will take up the water, but there is still no permanent insoak condition. A soil has a true sponge structure only when it has a mellow, velvety feel; when the organic materials are just short of complete decay and when this velvety condition is a permanent condition. Many crops must be thoroughly disked under and worked as deeply as possible into the soil. If one examines the soil in an old weed patch where there has been no flooding or erosion, one will get the feel of a soil with an efficient sponge structure.

In a very large number of cases, rebuilding the surface insoak is not the whole operation. Often there is claypan a foot or so below the surface which prevents the downward percolation of the water. Although the tiny dams and reservoirs have been efficiently built, the water does not go down. Instead, it "waterlogs" the surface soil. In such cases deep chiseling, or subsoiling, becomes indispensable. Indeed, to return the insoak to a great portion of our land, the chisel will have to come into greater use than ever before. It is entirely possible that special chisels will be required for this purpose. Before operations are begun on any insoak project, the subsoil should be explored for possible hardpan obstructions.

The small-watershed plan of insoak development is completely scientific and, what is equally important, psychologically sound. The small watershed will bring results on the individual farm, and it is manageable enough to be run as a neighborhood project. Everybody can play some part in the venture. To be able to talk about "our project" carries with it a kind of magic power. It gives one the determination necessary for ultimate success.

All small watersheds in an area must be harmoniously synchronized to form the larger and more extensive unit, otherwise there will be conflict of interest. Indeed, some operations must be carried out entirely in terms of the larger unit. There must be over-all water laws and regulations which will give justice to all and maltreatment to none. Within these limitations the small watershed is free to grow and develop according to local ingenuity.

The small watershed and quality water go hand in hand. When to these are added small reservoirs to hold the runoff until the insoak pattern is completely established, and to catch and hold excess water after insoak has been established, the whole pattern takes shape in a manner that spells lasting progress: water moving down through the soil segment of the cycle; water replenishing the zone of saturation. Wells of nutritious water will follow, and springs that fairly gurgle quality. In due course even the small reservoirs will be fed mostly by springs, thus providing more quality water for many uses. And the ultimate reward? Contented, industrious, healthy people.

Conditioning belts around water reservoirs in the not-too-distant future are quite likely going to be recognized as indispensable. Even with concentrated effort, even with complete awakening to the dire necessity of it, returning the insoak to our lands will probably require a generation. But there is one shortcut to high quality water (though not top quality) that is certain to be taken once people recognize its possibilities. That is the construction of conditioning belts, exactly according to nature's plan, around reservoirs which supply domestic water. The value of these conditioning belts, when correctly built and efficiently maintained, should be stupendous. They would stop runoff before it reached the reservoirs and allow the water to filter down into the earth through the spongy surface layer which they provide. It would be desirable to dam all draws and small streams so as to check their flow and force the water to spread out over the belts. Building and maintaining the belts would be major enterprises. The land around the reservoirs might be owned by the town or city, or leased for a long period. In either case there would have to be a supervisor on the job who knew how to build and maintain insoak conditions in cultivated as well as in uncultivated areas. Makeshift management would not accomplish the task.

Here an important question naturally arises: how will a reservoir ever fill with water if the water is going to be caught and sent down through the earth to the inland sea? The answer is that a large portion of the water would not be permitted to percolate on down to the zone of saturation. Underneath the conditioning belt would be perforated pipes which would catch most of the water and lead it to the reservoir. It would be caught after it had taken that first step of insoak which, as we have already pointed out, is the most important step on the way to quality water.

While such conditioning belts would not provide water of *maximum* quality, the water would be good water. The belts would, moreover, raise the water table considerably, and pumps could then be installed to supplement the reservoir supply by drawing completely conditioned water from the zone of saturation.

A source of quality water such as this would be within the reach of most communities. Even if existing reservoirs do not permit the building of complete conditioning belts around them, every gallon of runoff that can be put through a conditioning zone will strengthen the community's water just that much. Transforming erosion slush by means of conditioning belts would be a constructive step down the health road.

The only logical course is to build for permanency, according to nature's pattern: put the sponge back into our soils so that the rains will be caught and sent down into the earth where they are supposed to go; build small reservoirs in the upper reaches of the streams—and along the streams when needed—so as to impound loose water before it has a chance to reach flood proportions. Larger reservoirs might be needed farther downstream to curtail runaway water in the larger creeks and rivers. Then, with conditioning belts around our storage reservoirs, wherever that can be done, where water is maintained primarily for human consumption, we will be well on our way to the solution of our worst water problems. Best of all, health-carrying water will then receive the recognition it demands.

Memphis, Tennessee, has a water system that is outstandingly desirable. It is a unique system because its operation rests squarely upon one solid fundamental: nature-man cooperation. Nature's only road to quality water is recognized and respected. First of all, insoak conditions are taken care of in the drainage area. Insoak is given the right meaning. Though the Memphis water comes from deep artesian wells, from aquifers that are probably not supplied to any great extent by local insoak, the local rains are caught and sent down into the earth. This is sensible water management, whether it pays back directly or not. Wherever this conditioned water, which has traveled nature's conditioning highway, needs a bit of extra treatment to enhance its quality, this treatment is administered exactly as nature herself would do it. The water is sent through wholesome sand, where excessive carbon dioxide and stray bacteria which have slipped through are removed. Then it is stored in underground reservoirs, whence it is sent directly into Memphis homes. Quality water? This is quality water plus, for the pollution menace is guarded against, every step of the way.

In the Memphis water system there is a lesson for every city and village in our country. And there is also a challenging question which springs out of it: Have *you* explored your zone of saturation—your segment of the inland sea—to learn what it may have to offer in the way of quality water?

For accomplishing the enormous task of land building throughout our country, there is no more promising force than the Future Farmers of America, who are doing wonders in making the American people quality-livestock conscious. Let these lads now turn with the same vigor to repairing our depleted lands. Finance their work with some of the millions of dollars that are going into temporary dams and reservoirs—and watch what they'll do toward repairing the soil segment of the water cycle!

In many sections of our country there are encouraging signs of an awakening on the part of the FFA chapters to the need for land insoak. Insoak is becoming a common word in the Future Farmers' vocabulary. Son-parent cooperation may yet put into dynamic action what most adult conservation organizations are slow to push beyond the planning stage. We are, of course, speaking of *conscientious* Future Farmers, not the boys who enroll with the FFA to escape regular high-school study.

To illustrate, let us consider the work of one of these active FFA chapters, the chapter of the accredited high school of Wilburton, Oklahoma. This chapter—comprising true agricultural boys—is starting to do things with the soil. It's only a beginning, but nature and her soil-water pattern are receiving more and more attention as the months go by. A number of the boys, in cooperation with their parents, are discovering how closely land insoak is tied to successful farming, particularly during long periods of drought.

And this conservation activity is due to the tactful leadership of a far-sighted teacher who believes in constructive action, John Sokolosky. He not only is a successful and efficient Vo-Ag teacher; he wants to see activity in the field that brings results. To set the best example in land management and other agricultural operations, Sokolosky purchased a mediocre farm and proceeded to turn it into one of the very best farms in the community—solely by utilizing what he gave his boys in class. Today this farm, this efficient FFA laboratory, is accepted as the model for his Future Farmers and by his adult farmers as well, of whom there are many in his class.

Now and then one of his boys goes and does likewise, entirely on his own. Bob Shero, for instance, while still in high school, started to build a farm; he wanted to put to a real test the instruction he was receiving. Bob's farm was not a very good piece of land in the beginning. But now, as an FFA graduate able to spend all his time on his farm, Bob is making great strides as a conservationist. He's building the insoak into his land everywhere and whipping erosion on every acre—with nature at his side. His small dairy of choice cows, like John Sokolosky's cattle, was sustained on excellent bermuda pasture through one of the worst droughts ever to occur in that region.

Bob Shero has no doubt as to what a home farm should be: the source of abundant health-carrying food grown on naturally fertile soil; community activities that are fruitful; labor and leisure combined to produce contentment; and wells of quality water that are the result of following nature's complete water pattern.

8 Water and Weeds

During my early youth, I was constantly searching for proof that some weeds were truly friends of the soil as well as friends of the domestic crops with which they might be growing. My Pennsylvania Dutch mother would insist that all weeds should be unmercifully destroyed, but I could never accept the verdict that all weeds were villians. Often, after slaughtering some husky weed in the potato patch, or a clump of lamb's-quarters or ragweeds in the cornfield or along the path, I felt that I had killed good friends. Something told me those weeds were there for a purpose.

A moment of keenest delight came one day when my mother reluctantly admitted: "You know, there is something funny about it—everytime I find a pigweed growing in a potato hill the potatoes are bigger than they are in a hill

where there are no weeds. And there are always more potatoes, too. I'm sure it can't be because of the pesky weed. I
just can't understand it."

There was no doubt in my mind: the pigweed was re-
sponsible for those good potatoes, though I still wasn't
quite able to figure out whether the weed in some way
helped with the potatoes' water supply or helped it in some
other manner. But that the weed was always beneficial
was obvious. Almost always, when a pigweed did not grow
in or very near a potato hill, the potato harvest from that
hill was less in quantity and the potatoes were smaller.

A year or so later, a neighbor who usually grew large
quantities of potatoes decided that the drought that summer
was too severe for him to expect any potato crop, so he
made up his mind to care for only enough of his patch to
provide him with a few marbles for seed the coming season.
Most of his field he turned over to weeds, and these managed to make a fairly lush growth despite the long dry
spell.

It was early fall when this farmer got his shock. The
drought had been partly broken by a couple of fair rains
and, as the pioneer custom was, he decided to plow his
potato patch and prepare the land for a fall turnip crop.
Imagine his surprise when his moldboard turned up an
abundance of fine potatoes at every other round. From
that weed patch he harvested an excellent crop of potatoes,
whereas the clean area did not even give him the marbles
he had hoped for.

When I saw those wonderful potatoes pouring out of
that weed patch, I knew I had reached a turning point in
my life. Here I had proof that weeds were not the water

robbers they were accused of being. Not always, anyway. The weeds consisted of pigweeds, lamb's-quarters, ragweeds, thistles, pusley and a few others—all our most common varieties of the cultivated field and my old friends which I had long been fighting for. That potato crop was strong evidence that the weeds had been water helpers during a severe dry period when water in the soil would be most limited. No other conclusion could be reached.

Now the question was, just how had the weeds been water helpers? The pigweed in the potato hill, I found, was clearly a conditioner of the soil. Its vigorous roots opened up the soil and enlarged the feeding zone of the potatoes, so that the tubers could easily expand. Little tubers had a better chance of growing into much larger tubers, which wasn't possible where the soil was tight.

But it was quite another problem to figure out just why the weedy potato patch could turn off a good crop, whereas, the clean field was a complete failure. This same situation occurred several times afterward and with other farmers, which showed that the first instance was not a special one.

Therefore, it had the approval of nature, but how and why? In the end I could draw no other conclusion than that the weeds were in some way helping the potatoes to get moisture. Where the potatoes were growing on good deep soil—weedy soil—my root exploring satisfied me as to what was happening there: the weeds were sending their roots far down and opening up the soil to a considerable depth, so that the moisture down below was available to the potatoes. There was some sponge in the lower soils, and the "temporary saturation zone" contained some water, even when the weather was very dry. In the clean land the potato roots just seemed to give up, though there was living moisture only a short distance below—enough to support them had they been able to push through the dry soil to get it. In such cases there was always a dry layer through which the capillary water did not rise, and through which the potato roots could not force their way, even though the soil was not very tight.

When I ran onto an impervious clay layer several inches below the surface, I was at first stumped. Here, even the taproots of the weeds seemed to be stopped cold. But they were there, and after a lot of digging I made what was probably my most valuable discovery: the roots of my valuable weeds had pushed down to the claypan then turned sharply and proceeded along the top of the pan. I was about to conclude that they never did penetrate the clay, when I began to run onto a weed now and then that *was* going through.

Most interesting of all—and instructive, too—I found that there were almost always crop roots—corn or potatoes or green vegetables—following the weed roots right down into the lower soils wherever the weed roots had been able to penetrate the claypan. Apparently only one weed out of a great number would penetrate the pan—but what a friend of the soil, and the crops also, that weed was! Roots from other plants for yards around would come there and dive into the lower depths through the door which the weed root had opened.

I have made further weed studies across the years in many parts of the world. I have found that some weeds might be water robbers all the time, and even the good weeds could be expected to be robbers now and then; but under many, many conditions the weeds were water assets. That point is now completely beyond doubt. Often the weeds are able to provide the crops with moisture during a long dry period. Furthermore, those taproots of the weeds, which fail to penetrate the tight soils, produce laterals. Many of this huge crop of laterals will work their way through the stiffest of soils. I have traced some of them for long distances and, not uncommonly, have found the roots of other plants tagging right along with them. My investigations have convinced me that at least some crop roots, and the roots of many weeds, have a kind of affinity for each other. And water is the governing factor of that affinity!

Since those first years I have collected volumes of data to sustain my findings. For instance, a farm woman won the blue ribbon at the county fair with silverskin onions she had grown in a weed patch. She had not had time to keep the entire patch clean, and the onions on the part of her patch which she had managed to keep meticulously free from weeds were scrawny and insignificant.

Another woman, who normally canned great quantities of home-grown tomatoes, saw that the drought one summer was going to get everything. She threw up her hands and let her tomato garden go to weeds. Even the weeds that managed to endure the dry weather appeared sick. But, as things turned out, from that weedy part of her garden this woman managed to harvest enough excellent tomatoes to fill all her cans.

Then there were the shiftless farmers of the Cherokee Strip—the cotton minds, as my mother called them. When a severe drought struck the country, these shiftless individuals were about the only farmers that grew any corn. One might have to wade through jungles of cockleburs to reach it, but it was invariably excellent corn.

After I had studied the science of capillarity, I was able to interpret the wet spots I often found around the base of weeds very early in the morning. These wet spots were visible only during the summer months of a dry period, and they meant that the weeds were sending roots far down into the soil and were getting water there. I didn't realize at first that capillarity was taking place *outside* the weed roots, but that was exactly what was happening. The woman's prize-winning silverskin onions were able to grow to large size because of this capillary water. As for the tomatoes that grew during the drought, they were probably sending their roots down into the lower soils along with the weeds. Tomato roots are persistent prowlers.

And so, in returning the insoak to our lands we should not ignore the intrinsic value of weeds. Every community has indigenous weeds that are ready to play their part in improving eroded land. Many weeds are well adapted to that constructive work. However, because weeds are weeds, they are contrary if you try to plant them and make them grow. But their value is great enough to warrant any effort to get them to take hold on ravaged land. Once started, they will sometimes do wonders in reestablishing insoak. (There is one fairly safe rule for getting weeds to grow: always plant weed seeds on hard ground and do not cover them. Let the rain beat the seed into the soil.) Because our common weeds feed, to a large degree, in the lower soils, they are able to gather up nutrients which domestic crops normally do not get. The capillary water which they absorb there may well be a health link which the animal needs.

So, before we start condemning weeds because they are weeds, let us ponder a bit and see what meaning they have for us in nature's great water cycle. The naturalist has long known that weeds have a role to play in the far reaches of the mountains where lowland floods so often have their birth. They hold back snow and provide insoak conditions for the water as the snow melts. And all the way from the high mountains peaks to the low valleys, there are varieties of weeds that belong in the preservation scheme of nature: they help to build the water roads that lead to the inland sea.

9 Humid Irrigation

Applying water to soil artificially is as old as farming itself; yet, if you ask farmers exactly why they irrigate, their answers will reveal that most of them do not understand the full, scientific meaning of the process. They know that plants need water for life and growth, and so, if there has been insufficient rain, they proceed to apply water, perhaps in a wholly haphazard manner. That there are many wrong ways and probably only a few right ways of feeding water to growing plants rarely enters their minds. But they are not entirely to blame. Nature's method of watering the soil shows little evidence of being a regulated one. Farmers feel, therefore, that when drought comes, all that is needed is to pour the water on and leave it to the plant and the soil to rectify any mistakes.

This the plant and the soil will do, in time, but usually at the expense of the one who made the mistakes. Except in a few respects, rain and artificial sprinkling are not the same. Neither is ditch watering the same as a slow, soaking rain. But, if ditch irrigation or sprinkler irrigation is properly done, either can be made a close approximation of the rain.

Correct irrigation is a science, and a rather exact science at that. In a humid region, where in the not-too-distant future irrigation will be universally accepted as a necessary supplement to the rain, even in general farming, the practice of applying water to the soil as a rain assistant will be found to be a more complicated one than are the irrigation practices followed in arid regions, where there is little or no rain to reckon with in working out an irrigation blueprint. In arid regions, without the unpredictable factor of rain and the weather that produces it, it is easier to establish a stable irrigation pattern.

No one would expect to succeed in the dairy business without learning the intricacies of good dairying. Similarly, there are intricacies in irrigation—and many of them—that the irrigator should expect to learn. It is not easy to see that nature follows a definite water pattern for optimum plant growth, but such is the case. In all her activities nature employs balances and counterbalances. Too much water or too little water can be injurious to both the plant and the soil. The reason we apply water to the soil is to *assist* nature in maintaining her balance when things seem to go haywire in her water phase.

Now comes the first invariable rule: correct irrigation begins with land preparation. Even though irrigation water may be bountiful, to apply water to poor land is, in most instances, a waste of time and effort. Nature may spill rain on the just and unjust; man can't afford to do it. Immediately a farmer or gardener decides to accept irrigation as an established practice, he should start asking himself some very pertinent questions: Is my land conditioned to receive irrigation water? Is my soil sufficiently fertile to warrant the cost? What kind of subsoil have I? Have I an impervious layer a short distance below the surface that will prevent normal percolation? Am I likely to have the problem of waterlogging? These questions and many others should be definitely answered before the first dollar is spent toward establishing an irrigation system.

In preparing land for irrigation, one of two operations may be essential. First, the land should be leveled, if at all practicable. If this is not possible, the slopes should be made uniform. Even where the sprinkler system is employed, it will pay to have the surface of the land as uniform as it can economically be made. Second, and above everything else, the sponge structure should be established in the land through a complete "green manure" treatment. This will guarantee that insoak will take place properly and effectively. Where the insoak is right, it is an easy matter for nature to take over and deliver to the irrigator the maximum returns for the water supplied.

There are, of course, many systems of applying water to the soil. Those likely to be most commonly used in humid areas, as supplements to rain, are the sprinkler and the furrow. The furrow method, while probably the most ancient of irrigation systems, has very definite limitations. Land that has more than a three-and-a-half-inch drop per hundred feet is normally too steep for the furrow, unless, of course, one irrigates on the contour. Where land is sufficiently level and where the insoak is good, the furrow will more than prove its worth in carrying a field crop through those parched months of summer when rains in many regions are so often meager. This naturally takes for granted that irrigation water is available. In many humid regions, droughts occur during the very period when crops are most in need of water—when corn is in the tasseling stage, for instance. More agricultural failures can be traced to this dry period than to a great number of other causes combined. Often, just one soaking of the soil at that time can spell the difference between a good crop and almost complete failure.

Once a farmer has given his land the best preparation possible, he still needs to know what to do and what not to do in the application of his irrigation water. The kind of crop will govern the number and depth of water channels employed. The water spread into the root zone of the growing crop is the vital factor. It is very important that the main feeding roots of the plant be not above the bottom of the furrow. Further, if the land is excessively steep, the water will rush down the furrow without making the necessary side spread. This is an excellent illustration of the point that the mere application of water to the land is not necessarily irrigation.

In furrow irrigation it is a good policy to employ the largest stream possible without causing erosion. This assures the best water spread and permits the soil to take in water evenly. As soon as the water reaches the end of the furrow, the irrigator should start reducing the stream flow. The condition of the land will determine how rapid this reduction should be. As a rule, sandy soils should be given short runs, while in clays the run will have to be much longer. And one should not irrigate light and heavy soils with the same furrow. This means that the irrigator should prepare an irrigation blueprint for his fields so that each type of soil can be given the kind of irrigation it requires.

The irrigation picture will always stand out more clearly if one does not lose sight of just why he irrigates at all. His aim is two-fold: he wants to maintain the capillary water in his soil, and he wants to keep that temporary zone of saturation, that region just below the main root zone, well filled. This will guarantee a supply for the capillary flow upward and will provide a source of water for the plants that prefer to go in search of it. Applying more water than is necessary to meet these conditions will be waste, so far as the particular project is concerned, though the excess gravity water moving on down to the inland sea might enhance the value of nearby wells and springs to a slight degree. However, even this enhancement will occur only when there is no claypan or other impervious layer a short distance below the surface. Excessive irrigation, in this case, may develop a waterlogged surface soil, instead of the much-desired temporary water zone for maintaining capillarity. Commonly a good chiseling of the land at the outset will take care of this difficulty. A good irrigator will also see that water emerging from the end of his furrows is channeled into a pond or turned onto an adjoining field that needs it.

It is entirely possible that the sprinkler system of irrigation will, in time, become more universal than the furrow, despite the latter's hoary age. Like the furrow, the sprinkler has advantages and disadvantages. Possibly the outstanding advantage is that the sprinkler, though it costs more, is easier to install and can be used on all sorts of terrain. Then, too, the sprinkler makes irrigation possible on areas where only a limited amount of water is available, or on small areas where large ditches would be out of place.

On the other hand, and contrary to general belief, sprinkling, unless carried on during cloudy weather or at night, is not the same as rain. Many crops resent being watered when the sun is shining. Scalding and serious damage may result. Also, with sprinkling, an almost perfect insoak is important. If the soil is heavy and lacking in fiber, the falling water will produce splash erosion, which means that the soil's granulation will be quickly destroyed on or near the surface. The small particles will be pushed in among the large ones, sealing the surface as if it were smeared with plaster. All of which takes us back to soil conditioning and the necessity of establishing a good insoak.

As with any other operation, there is an irrigation system which is best for each type of farming. Especially is this true in the case of vegetables and flowers. For these intensive crops, an abundance of water is required at just the right time. Practically all vegetables need from five to six inches of rain per month during their most active growing period. However, the higher the quality of the soil the less water needed to produce quality vegetables. On poor soil, vegetables take up an enormous amount of water—which merely swells them up without doing much real good.

For the highest success in gardening, it is necessary that the gardener be subsoil conscious. That is, if his aim is to grow health-carrying produce. Good vegetable growth is as dependent on a subsoil of the right sort as it is on a correct surface layer. In building up a permanent garden area, it is important that there be that temporary zone of saturation just below the major root zone. This is taken care of by working the organic materials well down into the lower soils, whether the subsoil be sand or clay. If a gardener will follow this rule when establishing his garden patch and also in maintaining it, he will find to his delight that it will be possible to have good vegetable growth during dry periods with only a limited amount of water; or, in the case of many vegetables, with no irrigation at all. Here again, and with emphasis: it is better in the majority of cases not to irrigate at all than to irrigate vegetables on poor land. If the latter is done, one will just harvest water-filled produce low in quality.

If a gardener does not prepare his subsoil so that it will serve as a storage for water, then his subsoil should, in a large measure, determine his irrigation practices. If the subsoil is sand, or if it is tight clay, irrigation should be light and frequent. This is because, in sands, any water applied beyond what is needed to establish the water film just goes on through and is lost; and with clays, the pores are so small that only a small amount of water can be taken in at a time.

It takes preparation tillage to make a worthy garden. It is shabby gardening to plant vegetables on poorly conditioned soil. If the soil is dry at planting time, it should be thoroughly irrigated before planting. Planting should then be done as soon as the soil has dried to moist mellowness, and this moist soil should be pressed tightly around the seed so as to hasten germination. No water should be applied to the young seedlings until they are well above ground and well established. Wherever possible, the furrow should be employed in all preparation tillage, since this will put the water into all parts of the soil and do it quickly.

Where the surface soil does not contain a good sponge and where the sprinkler system is used, one can avoid splash erosion on small areas by spreading a thin layer of hay or straw or broken weeds on the soil before turning on the sprinkler. The water will then fall upon the organic materials and trickle through to the soil without any serious puddling. Save for the cases mentioned, vegetables should not be given light, superficial watering during a long dry spell. This kind of watering induces vegetables to root shallowly and thus prevents their reaching way down into the soil where the food materials, and water too, are likely to be more abundant.

Lastly, vegetables should not be forced by overwatering—as commercial gardeners are now and then prone to do. Most garden vegetables are a sort of paradox. They require an abundance of water to make quality growth, especially in the early stages of growth, but if given too much water they lose much of their nutritive quality. The excess water may improve the looks of the crop, but the appearance is likely to be very deceptive. This does not apply to flowers, since appearance is what we're after. However, many ornamentals—roses especially—resent wet feet, so a sensible practice is to apply water when needed, and in the right amounts, and let nature take care of the rest. If there has been correct soil preparation—how often we need that reminder!—which will mean a temporary zone of saturation below the normal root zone, a vegetable or flower grower will not need to worry over having irrigated too abundantly. Percolation will remove the excess water from the root zone—and send it on its way to the inland sea.

10 How to Irrigate a Lawn—The Ifugaos

In few activities do intelligent people reveal less intelligence than when irrigating their lawns. This is probably because they do not understand what the water requirements of grass really are. It is true that grass is not finicky in its requirements; nevertheless, it does have some special demands, and unless the irrigator is willing to recognize these, he is likely in time to find his lawn unsatisfactory.

The time to make lawn irrigation least complex is right at the start, when one is preparing the soil. Every effort should be made to establish a deep, rich, mellow root zone. In building for permanence, as one does when constructing a lawn, there is ample reason for putting forth every effort to get a seedbed that will not later show all sorts of weaknesses. A deep soil richly fertilized with well-rotted barnlot manure makes an excellent bed.

With such a grass bed, frequent irrigation will be unnecessary. It is vitally important that the soil be in a mellow, moist condition when the grass, either seed or rootings, is planted. This precaution will force the roots down, right from the beginning. Two situations, in even the best of soils, will cause grass to root shallowly: too much water in the lower root zone; and permitting the lower root zone to become permanently dry. A conditon between these two extremes is essential.

A good practice is never to irrigate the lawn except when the grass actually needs it. Needless to say, one will find it necessary to learn the water requirements of one's own grass. In maintaining desirable lawns, improper irrigation is more harmful in most cases than outright neglect. The common practice of irrigating the lawn daily, just to cool things off, is poor lawn management. Where a temporary water zone or storage region does not exist just below the regular root zone, excess water will either be harmful or wasteful, depending on whether the subsoil is clay or sand. One should make constant use of the shovel to be sure about all these important factors.

This will bear repetition: if the subsoil is sand or impervious clay, water frequently and lightly—but be sure to put on just enough water to soak down to the roots. If the soil is deep and mellow and the organic content is excellent to a good depth, it is best to water abundantly but only when the grass shows signs of wilting. When the grass is on deep, rich soil, it requires, with a normal sprinkler, about one hour and a half to satisfy the water needs. If the soil is chiefly sand, a little more than a half hour will suffice; but on stiff clay it may take four hours of very slow irrigation.

Keep an eye out for weak spots in the lawn. These weak areas may be due to poor soil or to insect trouble. As a rule it will be advisable to dig up the weak areas and replace them with new earth. The grass can be restored through either reseeding or transplanting. Do not get the habit—as many people do—of turning on the sprinkler and forgetting about it. Many a good lawn has been seriously injured through this practice alone. When water is scarce, it is wise to let the lawn suffer for a while before sprinkling. If the grass is deeply rooted, it will revive quickly once water is applied. After you come to know your lawn, learn what type of root zone you have and how to interpret its water needs on the basis of this knowledge, you can work out a blueprint for your purpose that will thereafter make lawn watering a simple matter.

Building and maintaining a lawn under permanently adverse conditions involves problems that do not fit into any standard pattern. However, this should not deter you from having a patch of green if you really want it. Some of the best lawns I have ever seen were built and maintained in such circumstances. Wherever there are a few inches of soil, you can induce grass to grow if you go at it correctly.

If the bed is rock, with little or no surface soil, haul in a layer of topsoil and mix it with at least half as much rotted manure. On such areas, you should plant only the most hardy grass that is known to do well in the community. As a rule, a mixture of grasses works best in such situations, and, with the impervious layer below, it will be important never to overirrigate. Waterlogging around the roots will kill out grass in shorter time than any other one thing. Without air, grass roots rot quickly. With six or seven inches of really good soil, if you are willing to take the pains, a lawn soft as green velvet can be grown.

The jungle savage can teach us the value of plant water —quality water number two—but also the science of water from the irrigation angle. In the rugged mountains of northern Luzon, in the Philippines, is the wild land of the Ifugaos. When the United States assumed control of the islands, the Ifugaos were among the most bloodthirsty headhunters in the archipelago. Yet these wild people possessed a water intelligence that had baffled engineers since the arrival of the Spaniards hundreds of years back. The cliff farms of the Ifugaos were one of the world's wonders, and the manner in which these "hanging gardens" were irrigated was an even greater wonder.

The Ifugaos are largely civilized now, and their marvelous cliff gardens have suffered from neglect and because of "educational progress." But fifty years ago these gardens were an unsolved mystery. In the hands of the water-wise Ifugaos, water always seemed to be a living thing, not just an inanimate liquid.

With no implements whatever, except the simplest of hand-made tools, the Ifugaos built their cliff farms tier upon tier and with supporting embankments built entirely of earth. Visiting engineers always gaped in wonder at those earthen walls, which clung to the cliffs like great swallows' nests. In a land where the annual rainfall often exceeded four hundred inches, one had a right to expect such earth structures to dissolve and float away. Yet those earthen walls resisted storm and rain as if they had been built of concrete. That much of the earth for building the hanging fields should have been brought long distances, a very little at a time, was in itself a feat much beyond the ordinary; yet all this was insignificant compared with the system which the Ifugaos had evolved for irrigation.

The water was led across deep canyons or along cliff walls in makeshift channels that were superb in their efficiency. Many an engineer, as he stood and gazed at those weird water canals, has exclaimed, "It simply can't be done!" Nevertheless it was being done, and marvelously well. Government men used to insist that the Ifugaos were the only humans who could make water flow uphill. In guiding the water from terrace to terrace, without permitting the slightest erosion, and without even a shovel to work with, and that too when the sky was spilling oceans, the Ifugao and his water manipulation revealed a water concept that was quite beyond the white man's comprehension.

No matter what we may be irrigating, a lone plant in a pot or a row crop in a large field, the basic aim should be the same: to establish the capillary water in the soil. This can be done in a completely satisfactory manner only when the soil possesses ideal insoak conditions.

11 *Romance of a Watershed*

Undisturbed by man, nature maintains harmony through her balances and counterbalances. The Great Plains, that vast strip of prairie and semiprairie lying between the Rockies and the Mississippi, were for unknown centuries the feeding grounds of one of the greatest arrays of wildlife on earth. Yet it is probable that no other section of North America was subjected to such contrasts: bitter blizzards in winter; sweltering heat in summer; periods of meager rains; periods of torrential downpours. Notwithstanding, nature, through her constructive laws—her laws of balance—provided abundantly for her hungry millions.

Periodically, however, nature was forced to change her operation on the Plains, and drastically, to maintain her balances. The grasses would succumb through a combination of drought and overgrazing. When this situation occurred, the prairie weeds with their vigorous taproots would move in and perform two vital functions: since they were largely edible weeds, they provided carryover food both through their vegetative parts and their seed; and they maintained sufficient cover on the land against wind and possible floods. In addition, the weeds opened up the soil that had been largely sealed by the matted grass roots, thus conditioning the soil for the return of the grass. When civilized man arrived on the Plains, he was staggered by the abundance of plant and animal life. That all this was possible because he had not been there to interfere with nature's laws of balance meant nothing to him. With his implements of destruction he started in to pillage and kill. Nature's laws of balance were completely ignored. The grass carpet surrendered to fields that were all too often incorrectly tilled; insoak was destroyed, and this destruction, in turn, resulted in the permanent drying up of a large portion of the springs—nature's normal source of quality water for both man and beast.

What occurred in the Great Plains, as a whole, is exactly what happened in most of the central and western parts of the Oklahoma Territory. When the first settlers arrived, Oklahoma was a land of extraordinary promise. The winters were cold and the winds swept frigidly across the western grasslands, but they were pure winds and free from dust and other contamination. The upper Washita River country, in spring, was a spread of thick grass and wild flowers. Old-timers will tell you there was something about the country that made you want to settle there for keeps. But the upper Washita, like other Plains regions, was a land of contrasts: there were the rolling hills, with their thin layers of soil; and the virgin bottoms, with their rich loams that reached to great depths. Even so, that earth of the hills was securely anchored by the succulent short grasses that had for so long been the favorite grazing grounds of the bison. Short grasses predominated on the hills; bluestem in the bottoms—nature's law of balance again. And the streams flowed continuously, because there was perfect insoak in all those prairies and valleys. The law of balance operated everywhere.

When we ignore nature's balances and counterbalances, we had better be prepared to accept the worst. Rolling miles of wheat are probably more exciting than endless stretches of grass. Besides, in those early days, as now, wheat was a basic food, and the Washita country was a segment of the world's breadbasket. The lands of the upper Washita had to fill their wheat quotas—along with other foods—and for decades they met their obligation generously.

But man, in his frenzy to reap from the soil, had not heeded the warning voices of nature around him. The streams started creeping out of their banks, after even normal rains, and the erstwhile harmonious stream flows were becoming sporadic. The once-clear creek and river waters, following a rain, were now laden with mud, a warning that should have been heeded by everyone, but wasn't. The water table dropped, and one by one the springs commenced to die; the wells grew dangerously low.

Then came the first disastrous flood! There had been floods before; floods that did plenty of damage. But this was the first killing flood, coming just after the grain had been put in the shock. Crops were swept away, acres of bottom wheat were swept from the land as though by a mammoth broom.

Finally, as one traveled over the upper Washita country of western Oklahoma, one was forced to wonder if there was much more that floods *could* do. Eroded land or over-silted land stared at one everywhere. Deserted homes were tumbling to decay. One crossed dry creek beds with scrawny vegetation growing where clear water used to flow. In the far West they would have called it ghost country.

It probably would still be ghost country had it not been for a few dreamers who were able to look beyond the hopeless situation and see the beckoning hand of nature; nature pleading for a chance to reestablish her patterns of balance. Today, in that changed upper Washita country, people like to talk about those dreamers, those men of vision. Almost always they'll start by telling you about one man in particular. He was a dentist, recognized as one of the best in the Southwest; yet Doctor Church could hardly ever be found in his clinic. Not because he had lost his love for his profession, but because he had become obsessed with the conviction that the cure of tooth decay among the end-less numbers of young people who sought his services could never be found in a dentist's chair. Both cure and prevention, he was certain, must be sought at the source of the malady—in the eroded, food-producing soils. To have healthy bodies, the food and water must come from healthy soil.

At first, people were apathetic, even though they re-spected the wisdom of the early dreamers of upstream flood control. Discouragement had eaten deep. "You can't afford to give up!" a few courageous ones would persist. "We can turn this destructive tide of floods and repair our lands if we'll all work together." And that day finally arrived when those stalwarts of soil conservation began to glimpse daylight. Under their combined and ceaseless onslaught, apathy and discouragement began to crumble—and soil conservation on the upper Washita had its birth. Nature's balances at last had an active meaning.

Today the Sandstone Creek Watershed is a shining example of what the persistence of a few can accomplish. This demonstration of the value of upstream flood control must be credited to those few men of vision who sacrificed time and money to prove that the old adage really holds true: to heal a sore you must attack it at its source.

If you visit that region now and talk with the happy, contented people, most of whom were ready to give up, they will tell you what upstream watershed development has meant to them. They'll tell you how it feels to stand on the brink of despair and how grateful they are to those dreamers and their supporters in the upper ranks of government: L. L. (Red) Males, Cheyenne banker; Doctor Lloyd Church, dentist; and two far-sighted Oklahoma governors, Roy J. Turner and Raymond Gary. They have brought contentment and plenty to a once-ravaged land.

It's an endless delight to travel over the Sandstone Creek and two or three other adjoining watersheds and observe what can be done when men cooperate with nature. It's thrilling to stand on one of those upstream dams and survey the benefits that scientific flood control can bring to a small drainage area: lakes of wholesome, clear water, so teeming with fish there is no limit to the sport. It gives one a sense of abundance to let the eye roam over the bottom fields, now producing lush crops with no damage from floods. There is quality water on Sandstone now, and quality food is on its way, for, under the efficient guidance of conservationists, quality is fast moving back into the soil.

Yes, they like to tell you about it, those watershed people.

Mrs. Auxion smiled when she met us at the door. "Oh, yes," she said. "We went through the worst of it, but I'm afraid I can never make you understand what it was like then." A light shadow slid across her countenance as she directed us to comfortable chairs. "My husband was one of the first to talk upstream flood control in these parts. I never did understand much what he was talking about. I only know we were having a pretty hard time making ends meet. You want to know what *I* have gained from the watershed? Before the shed, there was one winter when the only fuel we had for the old cookstove was dry sunflowers." I could see her expensive range through the kitchen door. "We actually burned dry cowchips in our rusty little heater—and we're glad we had them."

Then the warm smile came back. "I'm so glad that Mr. Auxion lived to see so many of his dreams realized. All his life he had wanted to fish, but never had been able to visit a place where there were any fish to amount to anything. I take it you saw the beautiful lake we have on our farm? For more than a year before Mr. Auxion left, there was seldom a day he didn't bring in enough fish for ourselves and some of the neighbors. Bass and channelcats—I don't remember the names of half of them!"

"And I see that you have beautiful flowers," I said. Mrs. Auxion's eyes sparkled. "I've always loved flowers, but never could have them as I do now. Would you like to see more?"

We followed her outside. As we passed through the screened back porch, she showed us an enormous freezer bulging with meat and fruit and vegetables—and fish.

The lawn was a soft spread of green. The many flower beds, some with mixed colors and some with singles, were riots of dazzling bloom. And there were bush roses and climbing roses, all as rich and sturdy as if they were growing in a palace garden.

At the gate, after we had completed our visit, I asked her, "Now will you, in the fewest possible words, tell us again just what this watershed project has meant to you?"

"I could never answer that question in a *few* words," she said in a low voice. "If Mr. Auxion were here to enjoy it with me—I think then I would have to call it just a little bit of paradise!" She turned and walked slowly back to the house.

We went to the upstream lake, with its green banks. It was something you'd remember. Some distance below the dam a large spring emptied into the flowing stream. Birds were singing in the trees all about us. "A little bit of paradise!"

They had told us that Robert Edgar was one of the busiest men on the subshed; never had time for visiting. We found him working on one of his harvesting machines. We assured him we didn't wish to interfere; just wanted to make his acquaintance and if possible arrange for a later visit when he'd have time to talk; time to tell us what the watershed had done for him..

His lips twisted in a sly grin. "Want to talk about what this watershed has done for me?" He started wiping the grease off his hands. "Listen—that wheat needs to be cut *now*. So you'd like to know what this watershed development has done for me? Well, that wheat can wait!"

We sought a comfortable spot in the sun. Then Robert Edgar gave us a heart-warming story of what upstream flood control had done in transforming his rather skimpy life into a life of plenty. He had worked as a hired hand during the lean years of the floods, and his wages most of the time had been pretty slim. But something kept telling him to stay with the upper Washita country; not to give up, even though it was pretty hard to hold on most of the time. He had stuck and saved his meager wages. When the bottom dropped out of land prices, he started in to buy with his small savings the poorest farms he could find. He couldn't afford anything else.

"After I'd gone to a few meetings and heard those who were trying to get people interested in watershed improvement, I was sure that things in some way were going to change for the better. It wasn't long before they did start to change—and they kept right on changing, and fast. Now, come along and I'll show you what upstream improvement has done for that poor land of mine."

Bob Edgar showed us what the watershed had done for a one-time farm hand who wouldn't give up: eight worthless pieces of land transformed into eight of the finest farms on the upper Washita; land leveled for irrigation and one of the best supplemental irrigation systems I have ever encountered—and in operation; soil enriched with sweet clover and other natural means—and insoak conditions established that equaled nature's best.

Robert Edgar is an insoak enthusaist.

As we waded through acre after acre of lush alfalfa and strolled down corn rows that gave promise of enormous yields, we understood the cause of his enthusiasm.

Although he is now a large-scale farmer, Bob made us gasp when he talked about his vegetable garden, which we had not yet visited. He told us he had built it of the right kind of soil and located it just below one of those upstream reservoirs, where he could give his crops just the right kind of irrigation. "For money? Certainly not!" he said. "I like to grow good truck to give away to people who have not been quite as fortunate as I have been."

Edgar, busy though he was, held us for most of the afternoon. He showed us how diversified, intensive farming can be a paying business on the watershed. And besides corn, wheat, and alfalfa, he is having success with hogs and cattle. He still works hard, but not because he has to. Like everybody else on the shed, he works hard because farming has become a pleasure to him.

People both in town and out on the shed call the Witcher Hatchers the millionaire farmers. And they probably are, though you wouldn't guess it when visiting with them in their simple, modern farm home. When we asked Mr. Hatcher how many farms he had, he just stared at us. "Why, gracious, folks—haven't the slightest idea!" And he really meant it. Witcher Hatcher is past eighty now, but, true watershedder that he is, he works hard because he likes it.

We had found him watering his large vegetable garden, several times larger than he needed for his small family. "I like to have good stuff to give 'way when folks come round," he told us. "Good truck, that is; not like what you have to buy in the market." Then he loaded us down with the choicest he had.

Before the watershed, Mr. Hatcher's choice garden was abandoned land.

He was one of the pioneers; he saw the wreckage of nature's balances and the tragedies that followed. He mentioned several now-prosperous farmers who had stood on the brink of want—and he included himself among them. He gives to sweet clover the credit for putting most of the richness back into his farms. He rates sweet clover as the prime insoak builder, particularly in the shallow uplands. Insoak is a word perpetually on his lips, and one can understand why. The opposite of floods is good insoak, and Mr. Hatcher is making sure there'll be no more floods on his farms.

It's not easy to believe the thrilling story of that Sandstone Creek Watershed unless one has lived through its changes: once-ravaged land and normally dry stream beds now boasting continuous flow of clear water; springs of quality water feeding those streams; the banks of the streams thick with healthy vegetation; belts of new timber springing up along all the water courses. And birds; birds forever filling the air with song.

For a graphic story of the evolution of the Sandstone Creek country, one can tap the memory of the long-time editor of the *Cheyenne Weekly*, John Cassidy, Sr., and John's wife, who were partners in the publication of the little paper that dates back to the earliest territorial days.

"Yes, I have lived through the changes on Sandstone Creek," he said. "First came those beginning years, when nature turned over to the early pioneers a land of abundance: deep soil and tall grass in the bottoms, and the uplands with their succulent short grasses. The streams flowed unceasingly then, fed from great numbers of clearwater springs. Fish were plentiful in the streams and wildlife abundant on the prairies. And the people were happy, although there were hardships, as in all pioneering. They were happy then because the Sandstone country had so much to offer them."

Then John was silent for a short while, as if living over again the period which followed the pioneering phase of the upper Washita. "It's a little difficult to paint a true picture of what began to take place as soon as that sod was broken up," he resumed. "Immediately that anchorage of the soil was destroyed, the Sandstone Creek country became a different land. Floods swept the unanchored soil down into the lowlands and silted the stream beds, causing destructive overflows. As I look back over it now, it seems that it was only a few years until the Sandstone Creek country was almost dead land. Certainly it was a changed land, and changed for the worse.

"It was about then that a few of us began to realize how desperate things were. We decided that something must be done and done immediately or the Sandstone Creek country would be lost for good. So we held meetings and pleaded with the people to face the situation realistically. We urged them to change their farming methods and make a start at rebuilding their eroded farms. It was tough going at first, for most people were discouraged. They were too discouraged to think of conservation. We also began pleading for help from higher up. For quite a while the government wouldn't listen to us at all. Our ideas were too fantastic, in their estimation. But we kept driving, and little by little more people began attending our meetings. Finally we won some recognition from people in authority—and then things began to unfold the way we wanted them."

John Cassidy is retired now from the publishing business. His son has taken over and is following in the progressive footsteps of his father. In his mellowing years, John Cassidy, Sr., with his still-active wife at his side, is able to survey the grand accomplishments which he helped to bring about. "You can see that gnarled old tree from here," John pointed. "There was a time when that was about the only tree in Cheyenne. All this refreshing shade which we now have is the result of watershed development."

"The fruitage of soil insoak?" I queried.

"Yes; and the efficient work of the men from the Soil Conservation Service. They've helped us to understand insoak and how to build it."

From one lone tree to a city enveloped in comfortable shade in the matter of a few years—that is a tiny pattern in the evolution of the Sandstone Creek Watershed. On the hottest days you can sit in the cooling shade in town, or on the banks of streams that flow night and day. You can sit under trees not far from some of those upstream lakes and draw in fish so fast you get tired baiting your hook.

Another historian of any region is the mail carrier, Gerry Davis, of the Sandstone Creek country. He can tell you plenty about carrying the mail, before the arrival of the watershed: constant floods and washed-out bridges and impassable roads. Mail carrying in the old days was one round of misery, he says. "Why, it used to take me three days to cover my route, I was marooned by high water so much of the time. Now I can easily make my rounds in two hours. This watershed development has done wonders for our country roads. From mud wallows, they have become highways you drive over in comfort—that's the difference."

Gerry Davis is high in his praise of the county commissioners on the Sandstone Creek Watershed. "You have seen how the upstream dams have done away with the old bridges that were forever washing out. The dams make the best of bridges, and the commissioners take special pains to keep these bridges in top condition.

"I'm eligible for retirement now; but why should I retire? Why, carrying the mail now is just a bit of wholesome exercise!"

The watershed brought good roads, he pointed out, and a rise of the water table which was providing an abundance of quality water. That, in Gerry's opinion, is one of the greatest improvements on Sandstone. And then there are the flowing streams that are calling back the wildlife that vanished after the sod was broken up and the floods took

over. Gerry Davis, being a pretty keen naturalist as well
as a mail carrier, sees the return of the wildlife to the upper Washita as a sign of nature's approval of what has
been done.

Roy Jones and his son Paul were putting the finishing
touches on the combine when we drove into the yard. A
panorama of ripe grain opened out before us. We explained
our business and said we didn't wish to interfere with harvesting; that we only wanted to make an appointment for
a later date. Roy Jones tossed his wrench into a tool box
and invited us to a nearby patch of shade.

"What has this watershed mean to me?" His countenance grew suddenly serious. "Well, for us it has just about
changed one round of disaster after another into a pretty
satisfying life. Sure, our wheat needs to be cut. It can
wait. Before the shed, it probably wouldn't have been
there for cutting. History? Guess maybe I can give you a
little of that. I was one of the early settlers in the upper
Washita."

Then Roy Jones unrolled that almost unbelievable history. He said he now owned twenty-four hundred acres
of good land. Most of it, he explained, had been built up
since the floods were brought under control.

A broad stretch of rich bottom land spread out in front
of us. He'd just give us the history of that, he said, for that
would reveal what it had meant to change from continuous
trouble to contentment.

"It may seem hard to believe," he told us, "but since we
have owned that land I have seen it deeply buried under
flood waters as many as eighteen times in one season. By

the time you have seen your best crop land under water eighteen times in a few months—by then flood waters become a sort of nightmare to you. And my fence-building history! Time after time I have seen a mile or more of fence go out in a tiny fraction of the time it took to build it. Before we got those floods eradicated I had mighty few nights of sound sleep; just worrying about what was going to happen next.

"But I sleep now, and wonderfully!" Roy's face showed that he wasn't just talking. "Thanks to those upstream dams, I don't have any more flood worries. That's why I always have time to talk about our watershed. Man, you just don't know what it means to lie down and let it rain all night—and sleep through it all like a log! And then to wake up and find your crops right there where they were —no, you just don't know!"

Roy Jones and his wife and son are strong boosters for soil conservation. It took a long series of disastrous floods to make them appreciate fully the enormous value of insoak. Now they know more about the value of insoak than the experts who visit them.

Mrs. Jones told us it just isn't possible to list all the values they have gotten from watershed development. A crude shack has given way to a beautiful rural house with all conveniences; abundant harvests where before it was mostly hard work and hopes that never seemed to get realized. Mrs. Jones's final statement rang with truth: "And we try to live our gratitude."

As you drive away from such a place, your ears ringing with the praise of upstream flood control, you cannot help wondering: why can't we have more of it? So much accomplished with so little—why don't we make it our number one project for the whole nation? Quality soils leading to quality water and quality food. In every state the eroded lands echo back the question—"Why?"

You listen to Joe Summers tell what watershed development has done for him—and you keep wondering if there is really any way of measuring such benefits. Joe Summers is almost blind now, unable to see much of the vast improvement that has come to the upper Washita. But he senses it all: the springs coming back, and excellent wells of nutritious, quality water.

He likes particularly to talk about his soil-building projects and his superb irrigation system. But Joe Summers can talk about those years of floods, too. He likes to tell about one flash storm that came near to bringing the end of the world to him. His chief farm interest at that time was the production of superior hogs, and he had gone down into the bottoms to look after his main herd when the storm caught him. Instinct told Joe to climb the tallest tree he could find and do it in short order. Clearly, Destiny wasn't ready for Joe to check in, for after the flood had subsided, that tree in which he had taken refuge was the only one standing. Almost a hundred of his choicest hogs were drowned.

"What does this watershed development mean to me? I'm getting along in years and my sight is almost gone. Even so, I doubt if there is a more grateful man on the Sandstone. One thing about a project like this, there is so much good that can't be measured in dollars and cents."

Gratitude on the watersheds of the upper Washita is real. Charles Plummer is an outstanding example of this. Charley's excellent farms are not quite on one of the sheds, but to hear him talk you would think he had been the greatest beneficiary of watershed improvement. "Whatever helps my neighbor helps me," Charley will tell you. Charles Plummer and his faithful companion, after rearing a family of ten, have retired now to a town on the shed.

We were listening to Charles and his ideas of upstream flood control—and gorging ourselves on strawberries and ice cream, the delicious berries coming from Charley's own patch—when Mrs. Plummer said, "Don't let me hurry you, but I do want to show you my yard and my flowers! This is the first time in my life I am able to have all the flowers I really want."

We finally got away from the savory cream and berries; then we went outside to explore Mrs. Plummer's gorgeous yard. It was the rainbow in manifestation. Mrs. Plummer at long last had been able to build herself a dream world of bloom. What has upstream flood control meant to the people of the upper Washita? Says Charles Plummer: "Whatever helps my neighbor helps me."

Mrs. Rhoton told us she started her farm life in a dugout. She had gone through the worst of those tragic years. Mrs. Rhoton has a beautiful farm home now, yet we could sense a note of loneliness in her speech. "My husband fought through the worst of it. Then when the light was beginning to shine through the darkness, he was taken away," she told us. "Of course, I'm grateful for it all; but I guess I'd be a little more grateful—if he were here."

A new land, a land of contented people, the Sandstone Creek country is today, along with a few adjoining sheds. And back of it all were those dreamers. E. B. Savage was one of the very first advocates of the Sandstone project and a member of the first Board of Supervisors. Mr. Savage worked tirelessly and unselfishly to get the conservation work going, though he did not live to reap the benefits from his labors.

And there were others whose names will endure because of their practical missionary work in upstream flood control in Oklahoma. More than that, those names will endure throughout the United States. Jess Dewees, a member of that first famous Board of Supervisors, from the inception of Sandstone spent freely of his time to make that section of the upper Washita the grand model that it is for other upstream developments. And there were still others of that historic Board whose names will be known wherever watershed development is accepted as the first logical step in the control of disastrous floods. W. S. Hiatt, Curtis Murphy, C. M. Lester all were factors in Sandstone's success. In the years to come, when upstream flood control is accepted for its true worth, this group of pioneer workers and practical dreamers, along with their co-workers, Doctor Lloyd Church and L. L. Males, will win high places in soil-water conservation history. Somewhere on the Sandstone Creek shed there should be a shaft bearing their names —lest posterity forget.

But it takes builders to transform dreams into reality. After a thorough study of the Sandstone Creek watershed development, it came home to me how much an efficient conservationist could do, once he gave himself completely to the job. This is exactly what those soil conservationists of the United States Department of Agriculture have been doing on Sandstone and the nearby sheds. The late Hugh Bennett was a visionary—a true missionary—when he established the Department of Conservation. It would do his heart good to see what has been accomplished by those Department men in transforming almost lost land into a region of plenty. Dreamers could initiate the idea of land improvement and flood control in the upper Washita; it took practical scientists to build upstream dams, reestablish insoak, and turn the destructive floods of erosion slush into saturation zones of quality water.

That is the kind of workmanship that will be standing for other generations to come and admire. That is conservation plus. That is the Sandstone Creek Watershed!

Glossary of Water Terms

A

ACRE FOOT—The quantity of water, soil or other material that will cover one acre to a depth of one foot.

ADSORPTION—Retention on a solid surface of a portion of a liquid or a gas.

AERATION; POROSITY LIMIT—When the condition of the soil is such that the spaces between the particles are filled with about 60% air.

AGGRADATION—The building up of any portion of the earth's surface toward a uniformity of grade or slope by the addition of material; especially the deposition of sediment in the beds of streams, and on the floors of bodies of standing water.

ALLUVIAL FAN—A fan-shaped deposit of sand, gravel, and fine material dropped by a stream where its gradient lessens abruptly.

ANALOG—Each old weather map kept on file for comparison with present weather conditions.

ANCHOR ICE—Ice forming on a stream bed.

APPROPRIATIVE RIGHTS—The legal right to take possession of a specified quantity of water.

AQUIFER—A section of the inland sea, or zone of saturation, that will yield sufficient ground water for wells, springs, etc.

ARID—A term applied to climates which lack sufficient moisture for crop production without irrigation.

ARROYO—A deep gully that is dry most of the time.

ARTESIAN AQUIFER—If the water in the aquifer is under enormous pressure so as to force the water to rise above the zone of saturation, the aquifer is artesian.

ARTESIAN WELL—When the water table is located below an impervious layer which is subjected to enormous pressure from above, and if a well is drilled down to the water through this formation, the water will rise above the surface, thus producing an artesian well.

ATMOSPHERIC CONDENSATION—The cooling point in the atmosphere where droplets of water (rain) begin to form.

B

BACKWATER SEDIMENTATION—Deposit of water-borne sediment in stream channels or on the flood plain above a dam or other obstruction, caused by the slowing up of current velocity.

BACTERIA—A large group of unicellular microscopic organisms widely distributed in air, water, soil, and bodies of living and dead animals and plants. One organism is a bacterium.

BADLANDS—Areas of rough, irregular, denuded land on which most of the surface is occupied by ridges, gullies, and deep channels.

BANK EROSION—Destruction of stream sides by stream floods, or by runoff pouring promiscuously over the sides.

BANK STORAGE—Water absorbed by banks of streams and later returned to the streams when the water table drops.

BASE FLOW—Stream flow that comes from springs, etc., in contrast to erosion water.

BED LOAD—Soil and rock materials rolled along on the bottom of a stream.

BOG—A stretch of wet, spongy ground.

BRACKISH WATER—Land water containing enough salts to make it useless for normal purposes.

C

CANOPY—The leaves and branches of trees and other vegetation which intercept the falling rain or snow and release them to the ground slowly.

CANOPY FOR RAINDROPS—Green vegetation or dead organic substances which prevent the rain from pounding the soil and thus sealing the surface, causing erosion.

CANYON—The fruitage of stream erosion after immeasurable time; a tiny channel grown to full size by erosion.

CAPILLARITY—The ability of water to rise in tiny, moist tubes or in tubelike channels.

CAPILLARY CONDUCTIVITY—Condition of soil that permits normal flow of capillary water.

CAPILLARY FRINGE—A zone saturated with water above the water table; the temporary zone of saturation below the normal root zone in good soil.

CAPILLARY WATER—The portion of soil water which is held by cohesion as a continuous film around the particles and in capillary spaces.

CATCHMENT BASIN—Drainage area. A small catchment basin is the area from which water drains into a farm pond.

CHANNEL—Passage through which anything flows.

CHANNEL EROSION—Erosion produced by confined streams in a watershed.

CHANNEL IMPROVEMENT—The improvement of the hydraulic flow characteristics of a natural or artificial channel by clearing, excavation or other means in order to increase carrying capacity.

CHECK DAM—Small dam placed in a gully or other water channel to decrease velocity of water.

CHISELING—The use of deep-running narrow blades for the purpose of breaking up the subsoil, to permit and encourage infiltration of water and produce better tillage conditions.

CLAYPAN—Impermeable layer produced when fine clay particles are washed down from the surface and clog the pore spaces in the subsoil. A hardpan.

CLIMATE—The sum total of all the atmospheric influences of a region which give that region permanent individuality.

CLOUDBURST—A type of summer rainfall in which an enormous amount of water falls in a few minutes from a disintegrating cloud.

COMPOST—Decomposing organic matter of plant or animal origin, which bacteria act upon to produce humus.

CONDUIT—Any channel designed to carry water.

CONDUIT FLUME—Open conduit used for measuring flow of water.

CONFINED WATER—Pools of water trapped far underground and having no connection with other ground water. Commonly seeps into oil wells.

CONNATE WATER—Water trapped in ancient sediments far below the earth's surface, sometimes dating back millions of years.

CONSUMPTIVE REQUIREMENTS—The amount of water actually required to develop a crop. Does not include water lost.

CONTOUR—An imaginary line on the surface of the earth connecting points of the same elevation. A line drawn on a map to show the location of points of the same elevation. A series of contour lines on a map shows the topography of the land.

CONTOUR FURROW—A furrow plowed on the contour on pasture or range land to prevent soil loss and allow water penetration.

CORE WALL—Wall built inside a dam to check percolation.

CREEK—Any stream next smaller than a river.

CREST—Top of a dam; top of a wave or highest point of a flood.

CURRENT METER—Device for determining velocity of flowing water.

CYCLONE—Any storm area where the winds blow spirally inward, with a calm region in the center. Normal land cyclones are not destructive.

D

DAM—A barrier to confine water for storage or diversion.

DELTA—An alluvial deposit formed where a stream or river drops its sediment load on entering a body of more quiet water, formed largely beneath the water surface, and often resembling the shape of the Greek capital △ (Delta).

DEPOSITION—The accumulation of soil material dropped because of the slackening movement of the transporting agent—water or wind.

DESERT—An area with an extremely arid climate. Also applied to any area from which fertility is exhausted.

DESICCATION—Drying up of parts of plant exposed to the air because of evaporation of water from the cells.

DESILTING BASIN—Part of a stream made larger, usually just behind a dam, to permit settling of stuff carried in suspension.

DETENTION DAM—A dam behind which water is stored so as to be released slowly through special outlets.

DEW—Moisture from the air that is condensed on objects that are colder than the air but not to the point of freezing.

DEWPOINT—The temperature at which dew starts to form.

DE-WATER—To remove water from water-bearing strata or other water sources.

DIFFUSED WATER—Water from rain or melted snow that has not yet reached a recognized watercourse.

DIKE (dyke)—Bank of earth thrown up as a barrier against water.

DITCH—A trench cut in the earth for irrigation or drainage.

DIVERSION—A channel with supporting ridge on the lower side constructed across the slope to intercept runoff and minimize erosion.

DIVINING ROD—A rod or forked stick used as a supposed aid in finding underground water.

DOWSING—Hunting water with a divining rod.

DRAINAGE—The removal of excess gravitational water from the soil.

DRAW—A shallow ravine that is a natural drainage course.

DROP—A structure that lets water in a conduit down to a lower level. May be vertical or inclined.

DROUGHT—A period of fourteen days or more in which there is not at least one quarter inch of rainfall in any twenty-four hour period.

DRY ICE—Carbon dioxide "snow" formed by compressing carbon dioxide gas. Considerably colder than ordinary ice.

E

EARTH DAM—A dam made of earth, or of earth and rock. Proper structure for upstream flood control.

EFFECTIVE PRECIPITATION—Total precipitation minus runoff and evaporation.

EQUALIZING BASIN—A small basin from which several irrigation furrows are fed water equally.

EROSION—The detachment and movement of the solid material of the land surface by wind, moving water, or ice.

EVAPORATION—The act of changing from a liquid stage to a gaseous stage.

EVAPO-TRANSPIRATION—Loss of water by both evaporation and transpiration.

F

FARM POND—Usually a hole scooped in the ground, the soil being employed to form the dam.

FARM WATERCOURSE—Any waterway entirely within the boundary of a private piece of land. May be either natural or constructed.

FIELD SATURATION—The filling of the air spaces of the soil with gravity water.

FILTER STRIP—A wide strip of vegetation around lakes and ponds to check runoff and either send the water down into the soil or force it to deposit its silt before the water enters a reservoir.

FIRST BOTTOM—The normal flood plain of a stream.

FLASH RUNOFF—Severe runoff produced by a sudden and heavy rain.

FLOOD—An abnormal flow of water overrunning customary channels.

FLOOD CREST—The height to which a flood rises or may be expected to rise.

FLOOD FLOW—The pouring of great amounts of water down a stream during a flood.

FLOOD PLAIN—Level land bordering a stream.

FLOOD POOL—That portion of water reservoir that is intended to impound excess runoff from its watershed, the object being flood control.

FOG—Tiny water droplets in saturated air, each droplet distinct yet so light it does not fall to the ground.

FREE GROUND WATER—The upper surface of the water table when it is under atmospheric pressure only and is free to rise and fall with changes in volume.

FREE WATER—The water in the soil that is moved downward by the pull of gravity immediately following a rain.

FRESH WATER—Any water other than brine or sea water.

FRINGE WATER—Water that is held in suspension just above the water table; the temporary zone of saturation which sustains capillarity.

FROST—Minute particles of "frozen atmosphere" spread over a frigid surface.

FURROW IRRIGATION—Irrigating by small ditches which lead out from a larger ditch.

G

GEYSER—A hot spring intermittently hurling a jet of hot water and steam into the air. Geysers are connected with volcanoes.

GLACIER—A vast accumulation of ice and snow more or less permament. Glaciers usually cover large areas.

GRASSED WATERWAY—A natural or constructed waterway, usually broad and shallow, covered with erosion-resistant grasses, used to conduct surface water from upland.

GRAVITATIONAL WATER—Water that fills the air spaces of the soil during a rain and later moves on down to the inland sea.

GROUND WATER; ALSO ZONE OF SATURATION—Water which forms an extensive reservoir or series of reservoirs below the earth's surface; the inland sea; the source of water for wells and springs.

GROUND WATER PHASE—The inland sea segment of the water cycle.

GULLY—The first channel or groove in the earth caused by run-off; contains water only during a rain.

H

HAIL—Sphere of ice resulting when a drop of water is carried in a circle and alternately passes through a frigid layer of air and a warm layer, freezing each time it goes through the cold layer. Finally the drop grows so heavy it tumbles to the ground.

HEADWATER—Source of a stream.

HOT SPRING—Hot water issuing out of the ground when gravity water sinks into the earth and comes into contact with hot igneous rocks.

HUMID—Said of a region when the annual rainfall, distributed throughout the year, is normally sufficient for crop production.

HUMIDITY ABSOLUTE—The actual amount of water in the air.

HUMIDITY RELATIVE—The amount of water in the air compared with what the air can hold.

HYDROLOGIC CYCLE—Water cycle; the circulation of the earth's moisture from sea and back to sea.

HYGROSCOPIC WATER—Water always found in dust which can be removed only with intense heat.

I

IMPOUNDMENT—Collection or storage of water in any given reservoir.

INFILTRATION—Downward movement of water into the soil; same as percolation.

INFILTROMETER—A device for measuring the flow of water into the soil.

INFLUENT—The inflow of water from a stream to some sort of storage place, usually underground.

INSOAK—Infiltration of water.

INTAKE AREA—The area where rains enter the ground to replenish the inland sea.

INTERMITTENT STREAM—A stream that flows only when it rains.

J

JUVENILE WATER—Water that is found with the rocks far down in the earth; mostly in volcanic regions.

L

LAKE—Normally a very large, fresh body of water.

LATERAL DITCH—A ditch leading off from the main irrigation or drainage ditch.

LEACHING—Separating ingredients from solids by means of water, as when rains separate valuable materials from a manure pile.

LEAKING WELL—A well whose casing is not preventing loss of water through leakage.

LEVEE—An artificial embankment for holding a stream in its channel.

LIMESTONE AQUIFER—The saturation zone when located in limestone. Such water is commonly hard and at times contains too much lime for normal use.

LOBLOLLY—Saturated soil resembling thick gruel.

M

MARSH—A swampy stretch of land ranging in size from a pothole to many acres.

MEAN ANNUAL RAINFALL—The average yearly rainfall for a region.

METABOLIC WATER—Water used by plants and animals for digestion and growth.

MIGRATION OF RAINFALL—Mean annual rainfall for a region is not static. It may work in cycles, as when the precipitation moves from the sea toward the interior, then back again, like the swing of a pendulum.

MINOR WATERSHED—A small drainage area, as of a single creek.

MIST—Water falling in droplets too small to be measured in a rain gauge; visible water vapor that falls.

MOISTURE STRESS—The tenacity with which soil holds water and will not release it to plants, as with hygroscopic water and the inner capillary film.

MUCK SOIL—A soil largely organic, dark in color, but light in weight when dry; spongelike texture. When wet, possesses a peculiar odor due to lack of aeration.

MUDFLOW—The mass movement of saturated soil down a slope caused by the pull of gravity.

MULTIPURPOSE DAM—A dam designed to accomplish several objectives; for instance, flood control, power generation, storage for irrigation or recreational purposes.

N

NAPPE—The frothy water overflowing a dam.

NATURAL WATERWAY—Water highway in ocean, lake, or river.

NEEDLE—A postlike structure set on end in an opening to control water.

NET CONSUMPTION REQUIREMENT—The minimum amount of water required by plants to grow and develop properly.

NET DUTY OF WATER—Term used by irrigators to express the amount of water delivered to land to grow a crop.

NET SAFE YIELD OF WELLS—The greatest yield that a well can give without bleeding the aquifer.

NON-UNIFORM FLOW—The changing velocity of water along the course of its channel.

NORMAL RAINFALL—A loose term employed to indicate the usual rainfall of a region year after year.

O

OBSERVATION WELL.—A well drilled or dug for the purpose of studying the variations in the fluctuation of the water table.

OCEAN HEAT—The high temperature found in the ocean at certain periods which commonly results in storms.

OPERATION WASTE—Waste of water in various ways when the water is being employed for a certain purpose.

OSMOSIS—The process by which liquids "soak" through a membrane where there are no openings, as when the water film passes into the root hairs.

OUTFLOW—The amount of water being continuously extracted from the inland sea.

OVERDRAFT—The uncontrolled bleeding of the inland sea in a certain area.

OVERFALL DAM—A dam built so water can overflow its crest.

P

PEDIMENT—Land located between the valley slope and stream.

PERCHED WATER—A small zone of saturation underlaid by an impermeable layer which separates it from the main zone of saturation or inland sea.

PERCOLATION—Downward movement of water through soil.

PERMANENT FROST—The term applied to the polar regions, which always contain ice and snow.

PERMANENT POOL—That portion of a multiple-purpose reservoir which is intended to retain water for an indefinite period.

PERMEABILITY—Capacity for being penetrated by water.

PERMISSIBLE VELOCITY—The greatest velocity at which water can be permitted to flow in a channel.

PLAYA—A low region in desert valleys that have no streams flowing through them.

PORE SPACE—Sum total of air spaces found among soil particles through which gravity water passes on way to inland sea; or the total water holding in the zone of saturation—inland sea.

POROSITY—The state of being permeable to water.

POTABLE WATER—Water that is safe and free from all pollution.

POTHOLE—Depression in the land that provide water for wildlife either part of the time or continuously.

POWER POOL—That portion of a water reservoir, immediately under the "flood pool," that is intended to furnish water for power generation.

PRECIPITATION—General term for all forms of falling water—or other forms of moisture—in the water cycle.

PUDDLED SOIL—A dense soil dominated by a singled grain structure, almost impervious to air and water. This condition results from handling of soil when it is in a wet, plastic condition so that when dried it becomes hard and cloddy.

R

RAINDROP—Liquid moisture unit in the atmosphere that has become heavy enough to fall.

RAINMAKING—The scientific feeding of artificial particles to clouds around which the moisture already in the clouds can form into drops and fall.

RECLAIMED WATER—Sewage water that has been salvaged by certain processes and reused for mechanical purposes.

RELATIVE HUMIDITY—The ratio between absolute humidity and the amount of water the air could hold before condensation started.

RESERVOIR OF GROUND WATER—A great body of underground water which, taken with others, makes up the inland sea or zone of saturation.

REVETMENT—A structure or obstacles placed along the edge of a stream to stabilize the bank and protect it from the cutting action of the stream.

RIDGE TERRACE—A long, low ridge of earth with gently sloping sides and a shallow channel along the upper side, to control erosion by diverting surface runoff across the slope instead of permitting it to flow uninterruptedly down the slope.

RIPARIAN DOCTRINE—The doctrine stating that the owner of land along a stream is entitled to all that water except what upstream riparian owners may need for "domestic uses." Domestic use is variable: it may mean only what is used in the household; or it may mean that, plus what is used in the barnlot.

RIPARIAN LAND—Land located along the banks of a public stream.

RIVER BASIN—The total area of land drained by a river and its tributaries.

ROOT ZONE—The area in the soil from which plants draw most of their food and water.

RUNOFF—Rainwater escaping by flowing over the land instead of entering the soil through insoak.

S

SAFE WATER—Water that is in no way contaminated.

SALINE WATER—Water that is saturated with one or more mineral salts.

SATURATED SOIL—Soil in which the pore spaces are filled with gravity water.

SCOUR—To abrade and wear away.

SECOND-FOOT—A unit of measurement of the volume of water flow; a cubic foot a second.

SEDIMENTATION—Consists of three operations: water tearing down the land and producing the sediment; water carrying the soil or sediment away; water depositing this soil where not desired. The third process is true sedimentation.

SEEP AREA—An area in which the zone of saturation rises to the surface of the soil. In seepage, water emerges from the soil over large areas, whereas, with a spring the water usually emerges through a single opening.

SELF-PURIFICATION OF WATER—Nature's own means of cleansing impure water through biological and chemical operations.

SEMIARID—Said of a region where there is some rain, but usually not enough to produce crops.

SHEET EROSION—The washing away of the soil in layers.

SHOWER—Light rainfall of less than half an inch.

SILT—Small mineral soil grains intermediate between clay and sand.

SLEET—Water freezing to ice as it falls.

SLOUGH—In humid regions, a miry, waterlogged area of land; in arid regions, usually a dry creek or river bed that flows only during heavy rains.

SLUICE—A conduit used to carry water at high velocity.

SNOW DENSITY—Water content of snow.

SOFT WATER—Water that is practically free from calcium and magnesium salts; when the latter are abundantly present the water is "hard."

SOIL EROSION—The detachment and movement of soil from the land surface by wind or running water.

SOIL-MOISTURE CONTENT—Actual moisture found in the soil at a certain time.

SOIL-MOISTURE RESERVOIR—The region of the soil from which plants get most of their moisture.

SOIL WATER—Water in the root zone above intermediate or temporary zone of saturation.

SPILLWAY—Conduit at a dam to take care of excess water.

SPLASH EROSION—Erosion caused by rain falling on bare land. Unless the land is very sandy the soil is puddled and the surface sealed.

SPREADER—A device for distributing water uniformly in or from a channel.

STILLING BASIN—An excavation at the base of a waterfall. It checks the velocity of the water.

STORAGE—Collection of water in any given reservoir.

STORM—Any disturbance of the atmosphere which varies strongly from the normal.

STREAMFLOW—All surface-land water. Surface reservoirs are confined streamflow.

STRIP CROPPING—Growing crops in a systematic arrangement of strips or bands to serve as vegetative barriers to wind and erosion.

SUBIRRIGATION—Regulation or use of the water table so as to bring the water up to the root zone. Nature commonly does the job herself.

SUBSURFACE IRRIGATION—Irrigation by means of underground tile or something similar.

SUBSURFACE WATER—Any water which enters the ground through percolation.

SUBWATERSHED—In a large watershed established for purpose of management, there are smaller units with each unit having a small drainage area. Each of these smaller units is called a subwatershed.

SURFACE WATER—All water that is drained from the land.

SWAMP—A large area of wet, boggy land, commonly with high, dry islands scattered through it.

T

TAILWATER—Water found just below a dam.

TERRACE—A ridge built across a slope to check erosion.

TERRACE OUTLET DITCH—The ditch into which the flow from the terrace is discharged.

THUNDERSTORM—The result of two bodies of air of different temperatures coming together in the upper atmosphere.

TRANSPIRATION—The passage of water from the leaves of plants out into the air.

TRAPPED WATER—Isolated pools of water far under the ground that have in some manner been trapped there in past ages.

TURBULENT FLOW—Flow of water which though flowing forward, is agitated so that small currents run in all directions.

TURGOR—The water pressure inside a plant that keeps it fresh and stiff. A wilted plant has lost its turgor or turgidity.

U

UNCONFINED GROUND WATER—Where the ground water is only under atmospheric pressure, it can rise or fall as the volume of the zone of saturation varies. It is then said to be unconfined.

UNDERFLOW—Movement of water through strata of inland sea; flow of water under any structure, like water under ice.

UNDERGROUND STORAGE—The catching of water at or near the place where it falls and sending it down into the earth to be stored for future use. This may be either in the inland sea, or man-made storage reservoirs beneath the earth's surface.

UPSTREAM FLOOD CONTROL—Control of water by means of two major operations: providing insoak to catch the rain where it falls and sending it down to the zone of saturation; constructing numerous small reservoirs to catch the excess water and prevent its pouring into the streams below and causing floods.

V

VAPOR—Water in an invisible form, carried in the air.

W

WASH—A gully; usually an intermittent stream, as found in semi-arid regions.

WASH LOAD—The materials which an erosion stream carries.

WATER COURSE—A channel occupied by a perennial stream.

WATER CYCLE—The circulation of the earth's moisture in all its stages.

WATER LEVEL—The position of the water table in a specific area. Overdrafts, for instance, lower the water levels.

WATERLOGGING—The permanent filling of the air spaces of the soil.

WATER RIGHTS—Legal rights to use water. There are three kinds: 1. Riparian. Rights which an owner has to a bordering stream. 2. Appropriated. Special rights acquired to the use of certain water based on given definite specifics. 3. Prescribed rights acquired by long possession.

WATERSHED—The present accepted meaning of a watershed is: a drainage area consisting of a few thousand acres, from which all waters of the shed drain toward a single stream. Smaller divisions are called subwatersheds; much larger areas are known as drainage basins.

WATER SPREADING—Any means employed to increase the ground water in an area. The purpose is to stop water and spread it out, then let it soak into the ground.

WATER TABLE—The upper surface of the inland sea or zone of saturation.

WATERWAY—A natural water course.

WILTING POINT—The lowest point to which a plant's water content can drop and the plant survive. If the water goes below that point, the plant will not survive, no matter how much water is given to the soil or directly to the plant.

WINTER IRRIGATION—Irrigating land between cropping seasons so as to keep the temporary zone of saturation full.

Z

ZONE OF AERATION—The surface layer of the earth in which the gravity water does not stand permanently; the zone where the pore spaces are filled largely with air. Varies greatly in thickness.

ZONE OF SATURATION—The inland sea; the zone where the pore spaces are filled, or supposed to be filled, according to nature's complete plan of the water cycle, with *Quality Water*.

Index